Life and Death of a Mental Hospital

Life
and Death
of a
Mental
Hospital

by Ezra Stotland and
Arthur L. Kobler

Seattle   University of Washington Press
1965

ACKNOWLEDGMENTS

Sue Davidson Gottfried deserves a special commendation for serving as editorial consultant through the early drafts of the manuscript.

We are greatly indebted to James C. Furlan, research assistant and human being par excellence.

We thank the almost one hundred people whose aid and co-operation are dramatically evident throughout the history.

This investigation was supported in part by U.S. Public Health Service research grant M–2858, from the National Institute of Mental Health.

CONTENTS

ONE   Introduction   3

TWO   Establishing the Hospital   19

THREE   The Identity of the Hospital   38

FOUR   Autonomy—A Full-Time Director   64

FIVE   The Board of Trustees   96

SIX   The Failure of Leadership—The Consultants   121

SEVEN   An Epidemic of Suicide in a Dying Hospital   160

EIGHT   Legacy   213

Life and Death of a Mental Hospital

CHAPTER ONE

Introduction

This book is a life history of the Crest Foundation Hospital, a mental hospital which was conceived in 1948, born in 1950, and died in 1960. There is no doubt that the character of each mental hospital affects the behavior and symptomatology of its patients, and that community factors influence the character of an institution—perhaps especially a mental hospital. Yet these facts are too often ignored in considering the problems surrounding those who are hospitalized as mentally ill. This volume is intended to give the reader some insight into the influence of community and institutional factors on patients in mental hospitals. But the report is aimed at more than that; it aims at the development of general theoretical propositions about institutions, that is, about hospitals and organizations in general. Its focus is on the factors influencing the hopefulness and viability of institutions. Finally, a basis for practical guides is provided, and practical suggestions, stemming from the theory developed, are offered.

Crest, as it is called here, was closely related to its community, and grew out of community needs. Columbia, post–World War II, had poor mental hospital facilities. The establishment of a new institution, one ambitious to carry out treatment of the highest standard, was a big undertaking. Crest started in an old, partially renovated rest home, with a small staff, and part-time professionals. The hospital developed quickly, and, in a few years, was considered an ideal or model hospital. Although it possessed facilities for only thirty patients, Crest's full-time staff was large; at one point the staff-patient ratio was three to one: three staff members to every patient. The professional staff numbered eleven. The staff people were well trained, and the educational level of the aides was exceptionally high. Crest's physical facilities were far from ideal, but the demand in the mental hospital field was for trained people and not for superb architecture.

From its high point, Crest declined. For example, in a period of one year the size of the professional staff decreased from eleven to three members. Later, Crest closed, and was mourned by many. Its influence on standards of psychiatric hospital care in Columbia was, however, very great, and did not pass with its demise. Many staff people, trained at Crest, went on to work in Columbia mental health agencies and hospitals. And beyond this, the standards for mental hospital treatment were raised by Crest's very existence, by its presence as an example.

The writing of the Crest history started with Arthur Kobler, a Menninger-trained psychologist with a strong psychoanalytic orientation. Kobler had worked at Crest for many years. Beginning in September, 1953, he was staff clinical psychologist, then chief clinical psychologist, and finally director of research. He had been engaged in research designed to measure change in the hospitalized mentally ill. By early summer of 1960, a year and one-half of a three-year grant period had passed and it seemed apparent that the research program was going to fail. Admissions to Crest had decreased markedly; the number of patients was thus too few for the planned research population. Also, some of the measurement techniques had proved to be unreliable. Following a progress report to the National Institute of Mental Health outlining the appropriateness of ending the program, Kobler was encouraged to take the third-year money for a radically different research program.

Things had happened at Crest which seemed to cry out for

investigation. Most particularly, there had been a suicide epidemic: from December 23, 1959, to January 19, 1960, a span of four weeks, there had been a suicide attempt, followed by the actual suicides of three patients. On June 22, 1960, another patient committed suicide. This suicide epidemic had to be viewed in the light of the past history of suicide at Crest. In its nine years and three months of life prior to January 1, 1960, only one person, in or out of the hospital, under the responsibility of the staff of the Crest Foundation, had committed suicide.

In July, 1960, Kobler started to interview staff members about the suicides. As a long-time member of the regular professional staff, he had come to know most all the employees well. Not being part of the administration concerned with patient management, he was in an excellent position to communicate closely with the staff and yet was not in such a position that they would be inhibited in their communication with him. Moreover, the staff felt strong inner pressure to communicate about the suicides, which had considerably disturbed them.

The major advantage of this situation, that of being intimately involved with the institution and the staff, was as well a major disadvantage. Kobler's deep involvement made him biased, and he doubted his capability of the objectivity essential for useful research. Also, while his general theoretical orientation toward mental illness is an interpersonal one and is concerned with the "field" in which the emotional disturbance developed and is treated, his background is essentially clinical, with an emphasis on individual psychodynamics. It appeared then that two needs had to be filled. Another person was required whose background and training were in the social psychology area, one who could study an institution comfortably and easily. Second, someone was needed who was not involved with the institution and who could act as a balancing factor for Kobler's overinvolvement. Shortly after the research began, Ezra Stotland, a social psychologist, became a consultant to the project. Soon Stotland was so deeply engaged that the research was completely a joint endeavor.

Both authors share a fundamental theoretical viewpoint: one cannot understand an individual, his behavior, or what happened to him, without knowing the social setting and other significant aspects of the environment. Emotionally disturbed behavior, like any behavior, cannot be comprehended if one disregards the setting in which it takes place. Plainly, we had to examine what led up to the suicide epidemic. Obviously the setting for the epidemic had been established before December 23, 1959. We kept moving backward in time, trying to choose a beginning point for the study. Each possible point in time seemed to have important elements preceding it.

With Crest's closing, in October, 1960, we realized that a complete history of the hospital was possible. The hospital's total existence of only ten years made the task feasible. Almost all the people who had been intimately involved with Crest and its development were in the community and available. We were especially pleased to begin at the beginning, since we believed that there were factors in the prehistory of the hospital which had long-lasting effects. We, therefore, decided to undertake writing a life history and set about collecting data relative to this new major purpose. We augmented our interview schedule, and set up interviews with new people, such as board members and consultants. We also reinterviewed some long-time staff personnel, this time emphasizing points relative to a history of Crest.

It is worth noting here that after Stotland joined fully in the research most interviews included both researchers. Our different orientations and backgrounds of knowledge enriched the interviews in many ways. Kobler knew the interviewees, had shared experiences with them, and therefore made assumptions of common knowledge, not all of which were valid; Stotland didn't know, and probed. His apparently naïve questions sometimes opened surprising new vistas for study. Kobler's greater familiarity with the institution gave him a much wider range of specific areas of questioning than Stotland possessed. Stotland's presence often seemed to help the interviewee to be more objective; the personal relationship between Kobler and the interviewee was less sigificant with Stotland there as a third party. His presence furthermore allowed Kobler to "sound off" more freely, to argue, to provoke, with the assurance that his more detached colleague was on hand as a check.

In gathering data we were extremely gratified at the cooperation we received from those who had been involved with Crest over the years. In total we spoke to eighty-three people for 140 tape-recorded hours. Only two people would not allow their remarks to be transcribed on tape. Only one was unwilling to talk about Crest, although he, a psychiatrist, was perfectly willing to discuss a patient in the suicide epidemic group whom he had seen in psychotherapy. Almost all the people—aides, nurses, presidents of the board, medical directors, psychoanalytic consultants—were cooperative. Often they were strikingly candid; always, it seemed to us, they were deeply involved. A very few were guarded.

People cooperated in other ways to assist us in securing additional data for the study. Members of the board and consultants offered us personal memoranda, letters, scrap books, and early records. Since the hospital had gone into receivership, many records were held by the receiver. These formal records of the hospital, including the minutes of the Board of Trustees, financial records, official scrap books, and more, were made available for the research.

The patient records, exclusive of nurses' daily notes, were placed in the University Hospital Medical Records Department, as were some miscellaneous hospital records. The University Hospital had accepted the materials under the condition that they would be available for research; thus, this information was made available to us. Also, we were able to "rescue" nurses' notes. With the closing of the hospital, storage of records became a problem. It had, in truth, been a problem before the hospital closed, and yards and pounds of daily nurses' notes were stored in cupboards and storerooms at Crest. It was decided that the nurses' notes were not important to keep, and the groundskeeper at the empty Crest was ordered to burn them. He did so very slowly. Later, the Crest estate and equipment were bought by an agency for a home for unwed mothers, and an ex-Crest employee found herself working again at the old grounds. She discovered, in the cupboards, masses of nurses' notes. Carefully trained, she was horrified that the records had been left in this careless fashion. She notified many people, among them her ex-colleagues Kobler and his research assistant, James Furlan. The latter dashed out to Crest, piled nurses' notes in boxes and transferred them to his car. As no one wanted the abandoned records, we took possession of them; perhaps eighty-five to ninety per cent had not been destroyed. We were not wanting for records.

During the early days of the development of the research, we regarded the project as a single unified one, although with two major points of emphasis. That is, we saw the telling of the life history of the hospital as the major theme, the major-minor theme being the group of suicides which we planned to examine intensively. We were aware of an imbalance in this plan, and of the fact that we had not defined satisfactorily the problems of organization of the data. Dr. James Tyhurst, on a site visit for a committee of the National Institute of Mental Health, strongly suggested that we separate the two themes. Dr. Tyhurst's arguments were convincing and seemed to offer a guide to the solution of the problems which had concerned us.

The two volumes, however, developed together, and there was much that each book had in common. For example, a great deal of data applied to both, and there were people whose involvement was with the two projects. Some of the data, such as specific details in the case histories of those who had committed suicide, were more pertinent to the suicide project; other data, for example, minutes of the Board of Trustees, seemed more vital to the hospital history. Most often, what was foreground data for one served as background for the other.

Early in the research we became concerned about ethical and legal issues. In writing a history of this sort, we were relating a tragic affair. This fine hospital, which played an important part in many lives, had died, disappeared, ended. There was a rash of suicides. In such tragic circumstances it is hard to avoid looking for someone to blame. Clearly, those involved could not have behaved in the most ideal and best sense; if they had, such a Shakespearelike tragedy would not have resulted. Some people were going to look bad, and we wished to make it thoroughly and absolutely clear that our sole desire was identical with the goal of those who cooperated with us in supplying information: to learn from this tragic experience.

We decided to disguise all individuals extensively, changing names and physical descriptions. Dates also were changed. Facts essential to the story would in no way be altered by these changes; the documents quoted would, of course, be authentic, but an individual's identity would be concealed. We consulted with professionals, such as Alfred Stanton, Morris Schwartz, and William Caudill, who had written similar volumes; and requested comment from the Committee on Ethical Standards of the American Psychological Association. Yet it remains true that those who were closely involved with Crest will recognize some participants in the events. We have consulted with the professionals who play major roles in the Crest story, and they have read the manuscript at varying stages. None has questioned the objectivity of the history.

With the publication of this volume, our project is ended. In 1964 the Free Press of Glencoe published *The End of Hope: A Social-Clinical Study of Suicide*. The two works are intimately related and yet each seems complete, independent of the other; each seems able to stand on its own feet. Nevertheless, they complement and enrich each other. This book is a history of a hospital; it is also a social-scientific examination of some socially significant issues. The sections which follow tell the story of Crest chronologically. The life of a mental hospital, even such a small one as Crest, possesses many levels and dimensions, and one cannot see it fully from only one frame of reference. Thus, within each section, each chapter focuses sharply on an area of interest.

The total functioning of a mental hospital as an institution, including lay and professional relationships with the local community, is studied and discussed in the present life history. We believe that the presentation demonstrates that it is not sufficient to study an institution in static, structured terms, merely describing pathways of power and communication. For a full understanding of the present, a study of origins and development is important. The reactions of the personnel of an institution to the social structure are certainly influenced by their previous experience in that institution. The past provides the personnel with a frame of reference for understanding and reacting to the present; it is a source of the ideology and expectations by which the present state of an institution is measured. In a hospital, social processes in the past determine the ideology about treatment at least as much as do some theoretical, intellectual, or scientifically grounded processes.

One of the themes in the present story is the ideology of treatment of patients at Crest: its development, the supports for the ideology in the face of problems and ambiguities, the changes and growth of this ideology, and the factors that influence change and growth. We use the term "ideology" in Webster's sense: a set of ideas about some issue or object, a philosophy. We are not assuming that the ideology has any logical integration—it may consist simply of loosely related ideas and attitudes. In the case of the hospital we are describing, the ideology would include such notions as: milieu therapy is valuable; psychoanalysis is a valuable theoretical approach; and psychological illness demands psychological treatment.

Ideology is not equally important for all institutions. It may be especially important when the workers are invested in the goals of the organization. It may have special significance too if the institution is young and wishes to grow, or if it is ambitious and aims at being special and unique. In mental hospitals strides are made toward achievement of the institutional goals if the personnel are involved, but it is by no means universal that they are. The oft-described "bughousers" valued quiet wards and power, rather than therapeutic effectiveness.

Crest was an ambitious institution, one that from the beginning strove to be best, and characterized itself as different and as good. The ideology was held intently, was believed in, and was considered important. Crest was felt to represent modern ideas and to be in the *avant garde* of mental hospital treatment. The care and protection of the ideology were important for board members and hospital staff members at Crest, for they all saw aspects of the ideology as distinguishing Crest from other, "poorer," hospitals, and as contributing to the unique identity that was Crest.

At Crest, too, the staff were intimately involved, at all times, with the institutional aims. From the very beginning staff members were committed, excited, and dedicated. As Crest developed, the ward staff became a close and intimate group, with their involvement in Crest of the highest importance in their lives. The professional staff too were close socially and regarded Crest as theirs, and as important. Later, when the hospital was on the downgrade, these close social groupings disappeared and authority levels became important in determining relationships. Suddently, differences between nurse and aide, physician and psychologist, appeared.

There is no question that the treatment and welfare, and progress and behavior, of patients in a hospital—any kind of hospital, though especially a mental hospital—are affected by the therapeutic personnel, by their behavior, beliefs, hopes, and expectations. A relationship exists also between the therapeutic excellence of a hospital and the effectiveness of its ideology and social structure in supporting hopefulness in the staff; for hope is an important therapeutic agent, and patients "catch" hope from the staff.

In both our volumes we are trying to understand complex social structural processes; we are concerned with the hospital's relationships with, for example, the community, and how these relationships tie in with, and influence, patient behavior. In one sense the problem may be viewed through a focus on a special sort of communication, the communication of hope. For the purposes of both volumes, the concepts of feelings of hope and expectation seemed particularly useful.

In the suicide volume we presented the thesis that actual suicide requires participation from significant people in the environment, and we stated that individuals who consider suicide as a solution are frantic or panicky, acutely troubled, feeling hopeless and helpless. They communicate their suicidal ideas and feelings to others: to those who are close to them, such as relatives, or to those who occupy positions of significance, such as physicians. The response of these individuals to the communication appears to us crucial in determining whether suicide will occur. A fearful and helpless response communicates an expectation that suicide is likely to occur, thus facilitating actual suicide. A hopeful, active response, indicating that change is possible, tends to avert actual suicide.

While the importance of hope for a person who is considering suicide may seem rather evident, since such people feel desperately hopeless, the concept of hope seems clearly to have more general usefulness. For example, Karl Menninger wrote:

> But we consider the crucial element in the Kansas State Hospital to have been inculcation of hope. Not in the patients directly, but in the doctors and all those who help them, in the relatives of patients, in the responsible officials, in the whole community, and *then* in the patients. It was not just optimism; it was not faith; it was not expectation. We had no *reason* to expect what happened and what still happens, and our faith was only that which all scientists share. But we did have hope.
>
> We had more than hope, you will say; we had had experience which encouraged hope. But these experiences were themselves based partly on hope, confirming the assumption that hope fires hope.[1]

Dr. Menninger's statement was supported by the experience at Crest. From the point of view of therapeutic personnel, whether therapist or attendant, therapy seemed more successful when people were hopeful and expected it to be successful. From the point of view of the Board of Trustees, or the hospital staff for that matter, hope in looking at the institution seemed critically important and positive expectations for the future seemed absolutely necessary. The institution had to be "sold" to the community, both to the lay people and the professionals in the community, and excitement and high hopes aid in selling institutions as well as other products. It is worth introducing here a theme we will discuss in more detail later in this introduction: truth on which hope might be based—reality—is not known. Hopefulness and positive expectations are attitudes, a way of looking at the future, and whether the future will be bright or dark is unknown. What is known is that such prophecies are often fulfilled; the self-fulfilling prophecy functions perhaps most successfully in areas of uncertainty of truth and limitations on the bases for prediction. Hope is a tender shoot, and requires

[1] Karl Menninger, "The Academic Lecture," *American Journal of Psychiatry*, CXVI (1959), 486.

a facilitating environment for development and growth. Social forces and individual people, sometimes acting in concert and sometimes in conflict, affect it.

At times, all institutions face difficulties, ambiguous and negative facts, even threats to their existence. All, then, must be concerned with sources and supports for a hopeful ideology, one which aids them to achieve their goals. You will see throughout the Crest history—and in the extended general theoretical analysis in the final section—the importance of these sources and supports. The reflected charisma of the Menninger Foundation, community members, and groups of outside experts, and the communicational and educational processes within the institution are some of the important factors influencing the ideology. And then there is leadership; perhaps, for an institution like Crest, the most significant facet of the interrelated complex of sources and supports, although one that is undoubtedly salient for all groups and organizations.

We regard the ongoing social processes at Crest as a drama in which all the actors behaved in ways they personally believed were in the best interests of the patients, of the staff, and of the community. In most cases their understanding of these best interests was apparently reasonable and valid. Yet no one participant at any time was so omniscient that he could see the "big picture" with its complex web of interacting people and forces. Some comprehension of the social forces and of the total field is necessary to understand the social processes which can lead to the collapse of a hopeful ideology. At Crest, social forces seemed so strong at times that individuals could do little to reverse the direction, even had they been able to grasp the "big picture." There were, as well, critical periods in the history of the hospital when the behavior of single individuals was of considerable consequence, or when a heroic effort on the part of a single individual might have made a significant difference. The role and power of the single individual, the leader, in institutions like Crest is a central concern of ours. How much difference does he make? What do changes in leadership mean to an organization? How does the type of institution, or the phase of its development or history, affect the meaning of the leader? These are a few of the questions, and there are many more.

All institutions may be viewed as being determined by people and social forces, with active interaction between the forces and the people. The character of the interaction will vary with other facets of the field. When an institution is, like Crest, ambitious, with people who are vitally involved with the aims of the institution, the encounter between people and forces will be dynamic. In such a situation the leader may assume special importance. And for mental hospitals a leader may have special importance because the mental hospital is one of the institutions in which there are no clear-cut criteria of success, nor are there sharply defined and agreed upon successful ways in going about the business of the institution. The general economic measures that determine efficiency in business are not applicable here. Nor, unfortunately, are the usual medical evaluative techniques. If one asks, for example, for a guide as to the optimum length of stay in a mental hospital one will find varying and extreme views. Some feel that the stay in the hospital should be as short as possible, the person returning to his home and to his community and his responsibilities as soon as it is at all conceivable. Others would say that the contrary is proper; that a person should stay in the hospital as long as it is "necessary." They will point out that it is dangerous to force too much responsibility on a person who is sick, and they would view quick changes as superficial. So, when is the patient well? When has the hospital done its job? Criteria vary and success is ill defined. In such a vague situation it may be extremely important to have a leader who inculcates belief, faith, and hope, and helps everybody feel as if things are going well.

We do not mean that there is no way of knowing whether anybody is ever helped in a mental hospital. Some people are helped in all situations and some are not. Nevertheless, it is often difficult to find out if one hospital or one therapist is good *relatively*, that is, in relation to another hospital or therapist. Techniques of research at different institutions vary considerably, as do criteria of change. It is hard to have proof of excellence. It is possible, however, to believe that the institution is doing excellent work. In institutions like Crest, it seems clear that it is important to those people who are involved with the institution to feel that they are doing good work, and it is disastrous to them—and to the patients as well—for them to feel otherwise. The fact that they cannot scientifically and systematically define and demonstrate the therapeutic efficiency of the hospital and of their work—of which they are fully convinced—is a problem which must be met.

Thus far, in considering the problem of the vagueness of criteria of efficiency of functioning, we have spoken of those who are immediately involved in the work of the institution; at a mental hospital like Crest this would mean the therapeutic staff. There is another group who vitally need a positive view of the functional efficiency of the institution, that is, the governing group. Governing boards of institutions concerned with the emotionally disturbed are commonly made up of important lay members of the community, with a few professionals. The governing group must "know" if the institution is doing good work or bad work, because they are responsible. Yet no solid criteria exist. Often businessmen are on such boards, and in uncertain situations they tend to fall back on the ways of measuring to which they are wedded in their businesses. These criteria are not necessarily appropriate. For example, Crest was not supposed to make money, but was supposed to be self-supporting. This offered a solid point of reference for members of its Board of Trustees, and, it might be noted, for members of the hospital and consultant staffs as well. Thus, the question that was everybody's daily concern for a long time at Crest was, "What is the census?"; in other words, "How many patients are in the hospital now?" The daily census was compared to what was then adjudged the necessary economic break-even point.

The question of whether an institution is doing good or bad work must be confronted, and the board may have to look to professionals for an answer. At Crest the board tended to depend upon the hospital staff who, as they themselves, were intimately involved with the institution. When the leadership is good, the leader may play the same part for the governing board as he does for the institution staff. In both cases he inculcates belief, faith, and hope. The board members are told—what they wish to hear—that everything is under control and a wonderful job is being done. Obviously, they will be much more comfortable if they believe that is the truth; and since they have no way of distinguishing whether that is or is not the truth, they may easily accept such information as an accurate evaluation of the functional efficiency of the institution. Moreover, they may, implicitly, request just that kind of report.

When the direct institutional leadership is absent or weak, the governing board is more anxious, and, in search of support, they may turn to outside professional people. These professionals are in a position where they may be able to view the institution more objectively. Their need to believe in the functional efficiency of the institution is not so strong as that of either of the other more deeply involved groups. In the mental hospital area, as we have noted earlier, views as to what is good treatment vary, and this may influence the opinions of the outside professionals. That is, the board may obtain a view of the functional efficiency of the institution without appreciating that it may be based on a particular theory of treatment which the board members are unable to evaluate. It is important to note that outside professional people, though perhaps more objective in the frame of reference through which they look, lack an efficient means of evaluating the effectiveness of the institution where criteria of effectiveness are poorly defined. In the situation at Crest, their answers were often made on the basis of limited experience with and knowledge of the hospital and were influenced by their own needs.

In this uncertain situation it can be seen how the function of leadership can become tremendously important. But there is more; for where leadership is so important, the leader has power. In the Crest situation, forces and individuals struggled for power among and between the outside professional groups, the community representatives—members of the board—and hospital staff members. This volume is a history and the true fabric of history is woven in the human situations. Power battles between individuals and groups can be seen, through one frame of reference, as dominating the picture of Crest, as they do many groups. C. P. Snow once wrote of a meeting of officials:

These men were fairer, and most of them a great deal
abler than the average: but you heard the same ripples
below the words, as when any group of men choose anyone for any job. Put your ear to those meetings and you
heard the intricate, labyrinthine, and unassuageable ra-
pacity, even in the best of men, of the love of power. If
you have heard it once—say, in electing the chairman of a
tiny dramatic society, it does not matter where—you have
heard it in colleges, in bishoprics, in ministries, in cabi-
nets: men do not alter because the issues they decide are
bigger scale.[2]

Power too, for good and for bad, is an intrinsic part of the
helping process, that central function of such organizations as
Crest. The problem of helping, in many forms, is a motif running throughout the Crest story. Patients came to Crest for help,
the hospital staff looked to the board for help, the board looked
to outside professional consultants and to other members of the
community for help, and so forth. This process of asking for help
is, again, not limited to mental hospitals; all organizations face
threats and need help at times. One facet of the helping process
which seems to us to be important is the attitude of the giver of
help toward the asker. The helper may view the asker as helpless,
"sick," as basically weak. Or his attitude may be one of regarding
the asker as essentially sound, as needing help to get over a crisis,
as having strength for the long haul. The first attitude produces a
situation of dependency; the second supports the autonomy of
the person or institution; and the difference is considerable. At
Crest, at different times of its life, help was dispensed in both
ways, and the consequences to the hopefulness in the hospital
may be seen clearly in the history.

Many of the aspects of the history of Crest as presented in this
volume may contribute to the contemporary movement of mental treatment centers into the community. For years, hospitals for
the mentally disturbed were placed far from populated areas;
those patients sent to the hospitals were wanted out of the com-

[2] Sir Charles P. Snow, *The New Men* (London: Macmillan and Co., 1954),
pp. 278–79.

munity, and were thought to belong to a separate world. Now mental health clinics are being set up in the community and good treatment is seen to require close contact with family and friends, with job and community responsibilities. To the establishment, and the operation, of the new community mental health clinics, the Crest history should make a contribution. The establishment of the institution is extensively described; the mistakes and successes are here to be seen, to be learned from. The problems of the relationship of a mental health institution to its community, and of the relationships between lay and professional people involved with the institution, are discussed at length here. Guidelines are offered, implicitly and explicitly.

It is our belief that we have presented here some conception of the whole picture, of the field, of the interrelatedness of issues, people, and forces. We hope this volume is more than a history of a mental hospital, and is, as well, a contribution to the theory of complex organizations.

CHAPTER TWO

Establishing
the Hospital

Crest came into being because of two psychoanalysts: Dr. Sidney Clark and Dr. Thomas Crawford. These remarkable men were stationed together in the army during the Second World War. Dr. Clark, who had a background of intensive clinical training in psychiatry, had been engaged for many years in private psychiatric practice in Columbia where his reputation and practice were excellent. Dr. Crawford, coming to Columbia from a senior staff position at the Menninger Foundation, Topeka, was the first practicing psychoanalyst in the area; later, he was among the first training analysts in the region.

During their army days, in 1943–44, Clark and Crawford discussed often, and eagerly, the idea of a psychiatric clinic for Columbia. They also discussed the possibility of better psychiatric hospital facilities in Columbia, although in their minds the latter took definite second place to the establishment of an out-patient clinic.

The close of hostilities found Dr. Clark at the Menninger Clinic, where he received formal psychoanalytic training while working as an associate psychiatrist on the senior staff. (His psychoanalytic training was completed after his return to Columbia.) Dr. Crawford returned to his Columbia practice. In the middle of 1948, their visions of a psychiatric clinic took form with the establishment of the Columbia Psychiatric Clinic.

Although there were partners other than Crawford and Clark in the original Columbia Clinic, and although the clinic itself was to loom large in importance for the subsequent hospital, only Crawford and Clark played significant individual roles in the hospital's history. And it is striking that these two associates, who worked so closely to establish both clinic and hospital, were of such different temperaments.

Sidney Clark is a man of strong ideas, given to expressing them strongly. He says of himself in this period, "I was a kind of firebrand." Dr. Clark is aware that his ardor occasionally leads him to make mistakes, but—"That's me. When I get going on something I think is right, I characteristically press like hell!"

Thomas Crawford is quiet and controlled, a man who thinks carefully before he speaks. Where Clark may be impatient for action, Crawford tends to exercise caution, to make action wait upon deliberation. In the period when Clark was "a firebrand," Crawford recollects of himself: "I tried to be patient, to remember that growth takes time." In contrast to Clark's warmth and engagement, Crawford's mien is shy, somewhat distant. Inevitably, the quiet Crawford gives the impression of being more tolerant than his outspoken colleague. Yet there is little doubt that Thomas Crawford is as firm in his views as Sidney Clark and that both men are equally devoted to the truth and validity of the psychoanalytic movement.

The founders of the Columbia Clinic aspired to give the highest quality of psychoanalytic and psychoanalytically-oriented diagnosis and treatment available at the time. And even as the clinic was being organized, the question of expanding it to include a psychiatric hospital and sanitarium facility began to seem real. Dr. Clark was still at Menningers, whence he was shortly to return to join the clinic. He and Dr. Crawford corresponded frequently about the future hospital.

The need for a hospital was clear; the psychiatric hospital situation in Columbia and the region, both private and governmental, was "woefully inadequate." Prior to World War II, there were two or three "rest homes" for psychiatric patients in Columbia. They were operated for profit, had no registered nurses, let alone psychiatric nurses, and no recreational or occupational therapy. Psychiatrists saw their patients at these places for a few minutes several times a week before going to their offices. At best, good custodial care was provided, with whatever other therapy stemming from intuitive understanding of patients on the part of untrained owners and attendants; at worst, the institutional objective was to keep patients "quiet."

In a note to Dr. Clark, Dr. Crawford wrote that in the hospital then being utilized by the Columbia Clinic, there was "some reason to suspect that some of the attendants . . . are using towels as choking devices for the control of disturbed patients." Furthermore, a recent suicide attempt had been "apparently caused by the fact that one of the 'nurses' disregarded all suicidal precautions, let the patient have access to a razor blade."

Their first plans, however, were modest. Dr. Clark wrote in February, 1949: "It seems to me as though if we could have a place well run by trained personnel and a quiet place where we can handle perhaps 24 or 30 patients more or less carefully selected, we could begin to attract some of the longer term patients and the better paying ones."

Dr. Clark returned to Columbia not long after this note was written. From this point on, the involvement of both men in the future hospital became almost total, even though the Columbia Clinic, begun so shortly before, was not yet stabilized. They continued their discussion and planning; they solicited advice; they considered building vs. taking over old sanitaria; they busied themselves with problems of financing. Accordingly, in the spring of 1950, they were ready to issue a confidential prospectus, intended as "an attempt to interest a limited number of key members of the Columbia business community in the creation of a foundation." The purpose of this foundation "will be to acquire and operate a thoroughly modern private psychiatric sanitarium and hospital in the vicinity of Columbia."

The prospectus was an interesting and rather open document. It chronicled in detail the inception, purposes, and subsequent growth of the Columbia Clinic, describing the personal and professional backgrounds of the partners. It described financial arrangements, the staff, and its ideals and methods of working. In this area the prospectus noted that:

> There was evidence on all sides of overly hasty diagnostic and therapeutic efforts during the war years, and at the same time of a greatly increased demand for the services of specialists in the fields of psychiatry. Although it was quite clear that any psychiatrist working alone could easily build up a very lucrative practice, the group of physicians who formed the clinic decided to join forces, even at the cost of loss of potential income in order to provide for more careful and more thorough diagnostic work-ups, for the mutual discussion of diagnostic problems, and of the assignments of patients to physicians within the clinic on the basis of the patient's individual needs in therapy and of the physician most fitted by training and personality to meet those needs. The physicians of the clinic decided also to sacrifice income to make more direct contributions to the community through teaching or through consultation services to social and other community agencies at reduced fees.

These, it might be said, were not only ideals but were carried out in practice.

In a section headed "Modern Psychiatry," the prospectus observed that psychiatry is "not all 'office psychiatry' by any means." It noted that hospitalization is often extremely useful, and can help people to return to useful lives in the community; further, private hospitalization does not require the legal complications and other disadvantages of commitment.

> Private sanitarium and hospital care does not simply mean isolation from the usual environment, on the one hand, or, on the other, avoiding the stigma of commitment; it means something considerably more positive in the way of active treatment by a highly trained staff and a full program of recreational and avocational pursuits specifically planned and individually prescribed for the

particular patient in terms of *his* illness and *his* needs for recovery.

The last section of the prospectus was entitled "Our Proposals." After a lengthy introduction describing the state of affairs of psychiatric hospital care in the local area, this followed:

> The Columbia Clinic desires to have its patients placed in a sanitarium where the standards and basic philosophy in diagnosing and treating psychiatric patients are as high as any place in the country. It is our aim to equal the type of care given by outstanding institutions. . . . In order to do this, several plans have been considered. The idea of using one of the existing rest homes and having it privately owned, as at present, but attempting to put our own concepts into effect has met the stumbling block that increasing service to the patient correspondingly reduces profit, and hence, if the rest home is regarded as a "business," such opposition is understandable. Secondly, it was thought that a number of individuals might be interested in acquiring such a hospital and operating it under private ownership with the understanding that the clinic professional staff would be able to put into effect modern psychiatric approaches in diagnosis and treatment. However, following the lead of other centers in the country, it was felt that a nonprofit institution which could acquire such properties or create them and operate them without profit could work in relationship to the Columbia Clinic, in that, while the staff would not necessarily be closed to other psychiatrists, the Columbia Clinic could have the determining voice in the attitudes and treatment policies toward patients. It could also furnish the professional services and assist in the setting up of standards, teaching, research, and treatment in the sanitarium.

A few months later, in June of 1950, Dr. Crawford wrote the "Preliminary Proposals for the Establishment of a Columbia Foundation." An early section, on the "Role of the Columbia Clinic," began: "Inasmuch as these proposals are advanced by the partners of the Columbia Clinic, we wish to make clear at the

outset the nature of our interest in a psychiatric foundation."
Emphasizing that a psychiatric hospital offering the highest type
of individualized treatment "should not be run for profit," the
statement continued:

> In the second place, we ourselves have no desire to own
> or to exploit a hospital; and we wish at all cost to avoid
> that type of situation in which the need to show a profit
> determines the quality of care that can be given to pa-
> tients. We do, however, have profound convictions as to
> the professional policies that should prevail in a psychi-
> atric hospital and we therefore wish a determining voice
> in the selection, training, and supervision of professional
> personnel in the hospital-sanitarium with which we are
> affiliated.

The partners of the Columbia Clinic, the statement went on, are
committed to service in the community; and they feel that one of
the greatest services they can render now is the creation of a
research, treatment, and training psychiatric institution. The
Columbia Clinic's desire to play a predominant part in the selection and supervision of professional personnel is "primarily in
order to have a uniform 'philosophy of practice' as well as consistent staff policies." Once the foundation was established, the
"proposals" suggested, it might feasibly enter into a contractual
agreement with the Columbia Clinic for the purchase of professional services at going rates. The Columbia Clinic would be
paid only for actual professional services rendered. Employees
would be employees of the foundation, but the medical staff of
the Columbia Clinic would retain responsibility for all treatment programs and policies, and for the conduct of all persons
dealing directly with the treatment, comfort and welfare of patients.

It appears that Crawford-Clark were trying to make their current position very explicit. They had abandoned the idea of a
wholly independent Columbia sanitarium, and were definitely
committed to a foundation, so long as they could maintain professional control. Their reasons for insisting upon professional
control are spelled out at some length, in terms of good hospital

practice. What is not made explicit, however, is the strength of the Crawford-Clark commitment to the Menninger psychoanalytic policies and philosophy as applied to hospital treatment. Dr. Crawford described this "philosophy of treatment [as] a psychoanalytic orientation with emphasis on 'milieu therapy,' as these terms were then used and understood by Menninger-trained psychiatrists and nurses."

The "Proposals" ended:

> Reverting to the question of the relationship between the foundation and the Columbia Clinic we propose once again that at the beginning at least the Columbia Clinic furnish to the foundation all professional services of psychiatrists, social workers and clinical psychologists. Nurses, nurses aides, attendants, physiotherapist, occupational-recreational therapist, maintenance crew and business staff, on the other hand, might well be directly employed by the foundation at the outset, but with all possible assistance and supervision of trained personnel of the Clinic. The reasons for this proposal are chiefly two: (1) that the Columbia Clinic already has available trained staff in the fields of psychiatry, psychiatric social work and clinical psychology, and this staff now gives services to our hospitalized patients; and (2) that it will be necessary to assure a prospective chief of staff for the new hospital that he will have a clinic staff appointment rather than the prospect of professional isolation while the hospital is being constructed . . . With expansion of the hospital and other foundation activities, it might be that all of these departments and functions would be absorbed completely by the foundation, and indeed the foundation might ultimately absorb the Columbia Clinic itself, but the division of functions suggested above is considered most practicable for the first few years.

It is noteworthy that neither the prospectus nor the "Proposals" was presented to members of the general psychiatric community. The presentation was made, with the exception of the partners of the Columbia Clinic, to selected individuals. Prior to

circulation of the prospectus, representatives of certain departments of the university in Columbia—the graduate school of social work, the department of psychology, the schools of medicine
and nursing—had been contacted for their views, and had responded very positively, expressing their hopes for the establishment of such an institution, in behalf of their own programs. But
while the members of the larger psychiatric community were
omitted, it was not due to their lack of concern about the psychiatric hospital situation in Columbia. Almost all the practicing
psychiatrists in the area wanted some change; some of them had
ideas for a "modern psychiatric hospital," and wanted the Columbia Clinic group to join with them in its development.

In their early correspondence, Drs. Crawford and Clark considered this problem. Dr. Crawford wrote that he and Dr. Clark
would have to decide whether they wished to team up with other
members of the psychiatric community, or "whether we shall
want to go ahead entirely on our own and start something that
we can control completely and build up according to our own
ideas." Their "own ideas" were of course firmly grounded in
psychoanalytic theory and its application to hospital patients as
they had seen it at the Menninger Clinic. And it was because of
this dedication to the image of a particular *kind* of mental hospital—"the Menninger idea"—that "our own sanitarium" finally
won out over possibilities of collaboration. Probably, in view of
the sources of their inspiration, the collaborative possibilities
with other psychiatrists in the community who were not psychoanalytically oriented were never really strong. (In 1949, two
psychoanalysts came to Columbia and set up independent practice. Prior to this, however, there were fewer than ten psychiatrists other than the Columbia Clinic group in Columbia. None of
them was psychoanalytically oriented.)

The nonanalytic psychiatrists then had little place in the proposed structure of Crest Hospital. Later, at an early meeting of
the Board of Trustees, when the hospital was just beginning to
get under way, the question of admission procedures to the Crest
sanitarium was briefly discussed.

> [It was] pointed out that any hospital retains the right to
> designate its own staff and to insist that admission to the

hospital be accomplished through a member of the medical staff. There was an informal agreement that details of admission could be worked out later in consultation with the hospital administrator and the acting medical director.

Clark and Crawford in their early correspondence and discussion showed themselves to be sensitive to most of the problem areas that existed for the establishment of the hospital, as well as those that were to be important later. They raised and considered issues of control of the philosophy of treatment at the future hospital, the relationship with members of the psychiatric community who were not psychoanalytically oriented and, as we shall soon see, money and relationships between professional and lay people as board members or investors. In spite of their appreciation of these problems, and prior discussion of them, each of these matters became a source of severe conflict during the history of the hospital, and none was ever successfully resolved.

Community support—both money and important people—was an early concern of Dr. Crawford's. In a memorandum to the clinic partners, he wrote:

> When our reputation as a clinic is established, we might be able to get a number of influential persons in the community to build for us. These persons could do so as an investment, but with a certain amount of public spirit as well. They would have to be "sold" on the idea that a good hospital and sanitarium facilities are expensive and that they would be meeting an important need in the entire community. We already have "good will" with several individuals that have access to investment capital, and it would probably not be too difficult to manage this in say two to three years. If we were to go ahead with such a plan we would have to plan carefully among ourselves as to how we wish to staff such a hospital-sanitarium and exercise medical control and supervision.

Dr. Clark solicited advice from the experienced people in Topeka. Although he believed that money-raising would be no problem in Columbia, the Menninger people raised certain questions about financing. One, Dr. Clark reported, "digressed on the question of having a sanitarium as a non-profit organization and as an answer to community needs and raising money by a voluntary subscription for such a hospital." Dr. Karl Menninger, replying "in great haste," stated that, "If it was going to be a question of men investing money in it for a profit, then we ought to tell them all that they would lose money on the venture." Another Menninger official, Dr. Clark reported to Dr. Crawford, brought up the problem of control over the policy of a sanitarium which might actually be owned by some outside lay investors.

In time it became evident to the two men that such an idealistic venture as they proposed could not be expected to clear a profit. Thus, in the "Proposals" it was made clear that the non-profit foundation conception was deemed most appropriate, with the strong statement that profit could not be expected from a psychiatric hospital of the sort the "Proposals" envisioned. At the same time, the early donors and board members were assured that the hospital would be self-supporting. Fund-raising for operations would not be a board function, although, implicitly, the raising of capital funds would be a function of the board. One early board member recalled:

> The original concept was—and Clark sold this very strong—set it up, get it going, and the need is so great and success is virtually so certain that it will be—and I think I'm recalling precise words—self-supporting.

Most board members, consequently, felt that they were not to raise money. But at a later date in Crest's history, many of the staff people, consultants, and even some board members, felt that the board ought to raise money for operations if necessary, since the hospital was not to be run for profit. This confusion over the money-raising responsibilities of the board was never clarified. The problem of money vs. treatment arose periodically in the history of Crest, and produced a real crisis toward the end of its life.

The "Proposals" suggests that control of general, and especially financial, policies of the foundation would be vested in a board of directors. In a lengthy discussion of finances, the "Proposals" estimates that $200,000 to $250,000 would be adequate to launch the proposed foundation. "It is expected that this sum can be raised through donations of from $5000 to $50,000 from a relatively few men and women in the Columbia area. . . ."

Clark and Crawford had discovered and investigated an old rest home, "Oak Hill," in the north end of town which was then for sale. They saw it as potentially right for the hospital they envisioned. The "Proposals" indicates that the operation of Oak Hill could be launched for about $75,000, with the remaining $125,000 to $175,000 probably sufficing to begin construction of a new hospital unit. The beginning accommodation would be suitable for about eighteen patients; fees from this number of patients would give a little surplus. With an initial capital of $200,000 to $250,000, the "Proposals" suggests, the foundation probably could function on a pay-as-you-go basis, although "the ultimate objective will be the highest possible quality of psychiatric hospital [treatment] *at cost* to the patient."

With the issuance of the prospectus and "Proposals" the tempo of the operations speeded up. Dr. Clark applied himself to raising money through a succession of personal interviews with a dozen or more wealthy individuals known to have some interest in psychiatry and in better psychiatric hospital facilities. Clark's appeal was couched in terms of the need for establishing good private psychiatric hospital care within reach of the Columbia area.

The largest single contributor to come forward at this time—with a pledge of $40,000—was Mr. Jonathan Bell, local business-man and philanthropist. He was to continue as the largest contributor, and to become the pivotal member of the Crest Board of Trustees. Because Mr. Bell's personality, motivations, and behavior had important consequences for the history of Crest, it is worthwhile to examine these as they appeared to others, in some detail.

Although Bell was already in his 70's at this time, he had been an athlete and sportsman, and was a rugged physical specimen— "he had one of the most remarkable biceps I've ever felt in my life." His mind was "razor sharp, and very well organized and logical." He was a powerful, persuasive, dominant figure, yet his behavior, typically, was not aggressive, but calm, quiet and attentive.

Bell's wife, an heiress, was also a philanthropist. She had been the moving power in the establishment of a community hospital. There was a widely held impression that Bell felt a genuine obligation to "do good" with his wealth. It was also observed of him that he seldom donated money for worthy purposes and then retired to leave the working out of these purposes to others. He wanted his "idealistic values" realized; he "would personally involve himself to try . . . to tie a string as to how his money would be used." Some, of course, saw this kind of supervision as springing from a desire for power: control for control's sake, rather than in the service of an ideal.

But Jonathan Bell's interest in psychiatric hospital facilities had not developed merely out of his general interest in "doing good." He had been intimately involved with psychiatric hospitals because of the long-term mental illness and hospital treatment of a close member of his family. When Crest came into being, this relative became a patient there, for a number of years. Indeed, some of Mr. Bell's critics have charged that the personal desire to install his relative in a good hospital close to home provided his chief motive for helping to finance the hospital.

It was observed of Bell and of another large donor to the hospital, George Britt, a wealthy businessman, that "they were really trying to make a place where their relatives could be treated." Again, so simplistic an analysis of motives can contain no more than a partial truth. But the point is important, because it brings to the fore a significant element in the dynamics of the institution: namely, that many of the donors and trustees throughout Crest's history were people who had relatives in mental institutions or in analysis, or were themselves in analysis. At the very least, this colored their judgments about hospital psychiatric care, about the role of the hospital in the community, and about individual psychiatrists. One board member, who was in analysis during his tenure, digressed upon this point to the effect that, often, he could not evaluate whether his judgment on board matters was activated by his transference as a patient or his responsibilities as a member of the board. He described the composition of the board as "a kind of incestuous group of ex-patients, patients' relatives, and people with a guilty conscience for personal reasons about psychiatry." Given the tensions generated in such an atmosphere, it is safe to assume that some actions taken by the board would not be altogether objective.

The second major contributor, Mr. Britt, was quite direct about the relationship between his personal problems and his interest in the plans for the hospital. Dr. Clark, he said, had "done an outstanding job when [other] psychiatrists . . . had failed" to help a close relative of his.

> And so I was grateful to him for what he had done there. And he told me of his dream and I told him I'd be glad to back it within the limits of my modest means. And . . . plans began to be put together that $75,000 would be enough to start a program; and I told him that I would give him the first $10,000, which we worked out through a little fund I have, on a loan basis, to be converted into a gift after it became tax-deductible.

An additional $5,000 was contributed by the Columbia Clinic, on the basis of $1,000 from each partner. Another $2,500 came from Dr. Crawford's father. Prior to this, however—in fact, almost at the beginning of the operation—a conflict was developing. The conflict was between the aspirations of Mr. Bell—characteristically attempting to insure that his money would be used in support of them—and the aspirations of the Columbia Clinic group, which were somewhat different.

Mr. Bell wanted what he referred to as a "community hospital." As one manifestation of this, he felt that the hospital should be open to all psychiatrists. Crawford and Clark, feeling a consistent treatment philosophy to be necessary, required some limitation on staff membership and professional involvement. Although this conflict never was completely resolved, some sort of *modus vivendi* was reached. Nevertheless Crawford-Clark remained greatly concerned about Mr. Bell's attitude toward their dominance in the professional situation. In May, 1950, Dr.

Crawford, noting the additional contributions by his father and by the Columbia Clinic group, wrote to Dr. Clark:

> This makes the basis of our appeal to others much less nebulous than it has been up until now, and if we can get one or two other definite commitments, we will have the beginning of a trend which will indicate also that this is not to be merely a pet project of Mr. Bell. I still think, however, that our position would be fortified if we could somewhere find a well-known younger man who would be working with us and for us, and yet sufficiently dissociated from us, so that the Foundation would not appear to be too much our baby either.

The "Role of the Columbia Clinic" section in the June, 1950, "Proposals" was obviously meant to clarify the difficulties between Mr. Bell and the Columbia Clinic—especially since other board members besides Mr. Bell were agitated over the question of the Columbia Clinic's relation to the hospital. Dr. Crawford recalls that, "Members of the board, notably Mr. Bell and Mr. Britt, reasonably took the position that they wanted to support a potential community enterprise, not a department of the Columbia Clinic." Nevertheless, some form of "closed staff" was agreed upon at an early board meeting, one in which the two chief protagonists, Mr. Bell and Dr. Clark, were present.

Later Mr. Bell demonstrated that he was not at all powerless. He had at his command a very important source of power and control; namely: money. He proceeded to use it. The financial pledges made to the foundation were originally made as loans. Mr. Britt, of the original big contributors, explained that this was "because you can't get deductibility on a new institution until it has been going for over a year." (It should be noted that Britt added that a loan "gave us a little measure of control over the situation, too.") It was planned that at the end of the year, when Crest should have been declared a nonprofit corporation, the loans would be made into gifts, which would be tax-deductible.

When the nonprofit status of Crest was declared, Mr. Bell announced his refusal to release his contribution to the foundation, and his intention of maintaining it as a "junior mortgage." The consequences of his act were manifold. Mr. Bell's move made it virtually impossible to raise more money. With a person of his wealth and influence holding out his contribution, it was difficult to approach others to give. One board member said that "this one single thing of Bell not releasing the money—if I were to say one single thing prevented other fund raising, this was it." Other board members agreed. "It would have certainly opened the door for others, I think, who felt that here one of the major board members and contributors maybe was holding back a little and didn't have complete confidence in what was happening at the hospital, so I'm sure that it must have certainly had that effect."

Mr. Bell's action had other effects. He was already held in some awe by fellow board members, because of his status in the community. The concentration of money-power in his hands, a result of the board's inability to attract other large donors, now further heightened his power in the Crest scheme. The other members of the board deferred to him and sought his approval on most issues. A board member noted, ". . . being a prime factor in the financial aid that came to the hospital, Jonathan Bell did say quite a little, and the board would vote accordingly."

Reactions to Mr. Bell and his behavior were not uniform, however. While some saw him as domineering and power-hungry, a psychiatrist at the Columbia Clinic described him as "a fine old gentleman." "He was always kind of worried about the Columbia Clinic's interest in Crest and whether or not we were somehow getting a rake off from it . . . but I mean I think most people liked him even though he was this way about it." Others pointed out that although Mr. Bell withheld his primary gift, he contributed generously to Crest on a regular basis, supporting the patient-aid fund, for example, at one time in the amount of $125 per week. Still others, on the board, were "ready to murder him," because of the position in which he had put them through his withholding of the money. These differing and ambivalent attitudes toward Mr. Bell were a divisive factor at many levels.

Thus, the board did not feel free to approach other donors,

once Mr. Bell decided to withhold his gift. Further, Mr. Bell successfully urged upon the board a conscious policy of refraining, at the beginning, from attempting to secure other large contributors. Both board and hospital should remain small, it was decided, until Crest became a "going concern," until it had "proved itself"—until, in short, it had something tangible to demonstrate as a basis for commanding wider community support. Dr. Crawford confirms this:

> Once the board was formed it became a matter of policy, during the early years, *not* to solicit widespread community support. Mr. Bell insisted, and I think Mr. Britt and others agreed, that Crest should become a "going concern" before the community at large could be interested in more than sporadic interest and financial support.

The first preliminary meeting of incorporators interested in forming a psychiatric foundation was held on June 16, 1950. Dr. Clark chaired the meeting, which included Dr. Crawford and six community businessmen, including Mr. Bell, Mr. Britt, and Mr. Bell's lawyer, Mr. Donald Conley. Dr. Charles Barclay, a prominent and highly respected local surgeon, while not present, had agreed to act as a trustee. A sum of $57,000 had been raised. The group now judged it necessary to bring this figure up to $75,000. The figure of $200,000 to $250,000, mentioned in the original "Proposals," was not referred to at this meeting, nor, indeed, ever again. It was estimated that there would be working capital of $11,000 once Oak Hill was purchased. An immediate need was voiced for securing commitments from varying individuals for loans to the foundation.

The same group convened on June 25, 1950. They had secured an additional $1,000, looked over the articles of incorporation for the proposed foundation, and begun to set up a committee to locate a man to act as hospital administrator. The first project of the foundation would be the construction of a modern psychiatric hospital. The "Proposals" suggests a population plan of 40 to 45 patients. It recommended, on the basis of a survey of the area, that a privately owned rest home, Oak Hill, be pur-

chased for about $65,000; the use of its present facilities some-
what altered; immediate appointment of one full-time psychiatrist, one or more full-time psychiatric nurses, and other needed
personnel; construction as rapidly as possible of a sixty- to sev-
enty-five bed modern hospital building. A decision to purchase
Oak Hill was made on June 30. On July 1, 1950, the Articles of
Incorporation of Crest Foundation, Inc., were approved by the
Secretary of State.

On July 14, the committee recommended the appointment of
Mr. Martin Johnson, a bright, ambitious, young businessman, as
hospital administrator, and he was hired. At this meeting, too,
hospital costs were discussed, and a tentative timetable was set
for beginning work on alterations at Oak Hill, so that patients
could be admitted to the sanitarium. By August 17, a superintendent of nurses, Mrs. Amy Stark, had been hired; the property had
been bought, architects had reported that about two weeks were
needed for alterations to make the Oak Hill property suitable for
use for patients. It was also decided that $90 a week be charged
patients for the use of facilities furnished by the foundation.

The preliminary foundation budget allowed for about $240 a
month for a part-time medical director. Dr. James Dean, a young
Menninger-trained psychiatrist who was in psychoanalytic training, and was a junior member of the Columbia Clinic staff, was
appointed part-time medical director of the Crest Foundation
"for approximately ten hours per week at a cost not to exceed
$7.50 per hour." This was, of course, a strikingly low figure—
which, one would suppose, should have been reassuring to Mr.
Bell, Mr. Britt, and others of the board who were troubled by
suspicions that the Columbia Clinic hoped to profit by its association with the hospital.

At the meeting of September 14, 1950, the attention of the
trustees was called to the publicity releases published on Sunday,
September 12, 1950. Mr. Johnson reported that sanitarium personnel would begin work on Thursday, September 16, 1950. On
the payroll at that time would be two male attendants, four female attendants, one cook, one caretaker, the head nurse, an
assistant nurse, an occupational-recreational therapist, the part-
time medical director, and the administrator. Five additional at-

tendants would be needed to complete the staff necessary for the care of fifteen patients, and an estimated five more would be required when the sanitarium capacity should be increased to twenty-two. September 23, 1950, had been tentatively scheduled as the date for first receiving patients. Seven patients of the Columbia Clinic then hospitalized would be shifted to the new sanitarium. Only three of these would be able to pay the full rate; the other four could pay no more than $70 a week. This charge was approved.

At this meeting Dr. Dean discussed his concept of his responsibilities in relation to the Board of Trustees; the hospital administrator and other hospital personnel; the chief consultant, Dr. Clark; the chief nurse; and others concerned with the operation of the hospital and the treatment of patients. He indicated that his responsibility would include in-service training of hospital personnel; medical supervision of treatment in the hospital; and liaison work between various members of the professional staff, on the one hand, and the administrator and the Board of Trustees on the other.

Crest was under way; the hospital was about to begin operation. The institution had been established with amazing rapidity. It seems clear that the factor most responsible for this feat was the deep involvement of three men: Clark, Crawford, and Bell. Each was highly motivated—even driven; and in each there seems to have been a combination of personal and altruistic objectives. All three were highly idealistic—the professional people with their desire to set up an ideal treatment center, and Mr. Bell with his philanthropic goals. At the same time, all three were desirous of "power," in some sense of the word. This is reflected in the many uniform comments about them: "You've probably heard it from others, but Sid [Clark] kind of thought that Crest was his baby." "I think everybody that I knew who was in on the beginning thought of Crest as sort of Tom's [Crawford] baby." "I think he [Bell] wanted to be the figure about which the hospital revolved."

In retrospect, one can see that the idealism, drive, and energy of these people brought about the establishment of the foundation and hospital, and laid the groundwork for the determined spirit and high purpose which were to dominate Crest for a long while. Their very enthusiasm, however, perhaps prevented them from giving adequate weight to problems which later had great significance.

CHAPTER THREE

The Identity
of the Hospital

> I remember the first staff conference out at Crest. Sid
> Clark was the consultant. . . . And I remember Sid—I
> forget how he said it—but something about, someone
> should take a picture here, and we should have our pic-
> ture hung on the wall; so that in generations to come,
> when this is a famous place—well, this will be us sitting at
> the first staff conference.

For those associated with Crest in the early years, statements of
the kind quoted above are typical. Crest Hospital was seen as a
new, different, and exciting experiment; as an institution superior to other mental institutions; and as one which had a his-
tory-making future. The Crest identity began to emerge at once:
it was, in the minds of those involved with it, a unique, valuable,
trail-blazing institution.

The hospital was formally opened to patients on September
23, 1950. Eleven patients, all under care of Columbia Clinic
psychiatrists, were received on that date. Dr. Sidney Clark recol-
lected:

> I remember the day the hospital opened. . . . all our pa-
> tients on our service at Maple Leaf Sanitarium—eleven,
> twelve, or thirteen—were moved to Crest one day. They
> were laughing and some were crying. They were so en-
> thusiastic about the whole thing; everybody pitched in
> and worked. It was a wonderful atmosphere.

His enthusiasm and that of Dr. Crawford carried over to the rest
of the professional personnel. Dr. Dean was assisted by the part-
time services of Dr. Richard Jones who, like Dean, was young,
Menninger trained, and a member of the Columbia Clinic staff.
Jones recalls:

> It was such a one-horse, two-bit operation in many re-
> spects out there. I mean personnel had to work double
> shifts, and there was nothing smooth about it. We were
> very hard up. It was a shabby place. But the patients
> caught fire with us. I mean, the fact that we were strug-
> gling toward people, kind of—patients. . . .

Dr. Jones became deeply involved with the institution very
quickly. "I chose a house out near Crest when I first rented, and
then bought one later, not far from it, in order to be handy to
Crest." Other staff members, he relates, were as involved, as
"sold" on the uniqueness and superiority of Crest as he.

> Everybody. There was a real *esprit de corps*. And the
> thing that characterized that *esprit de corps* was—as far as
> I can recall . . . all of us would gladly stay weekends,
> work late in the evening. Getting off on Saturday after-
> noon was a laugh. We never did, and we didn't really
> expect to; and we really didn't want to. We had more fun
> working—and in that way, those early months out there I
> cherished, as really liking your work and feeling that you
> are going to . . . that there is something great that will
> eventually evolve.
>
> I don't think I had any doubts in those days that Crest
> offered a far superior chance for a patient to get well than
> any other place I knew of in the area. And I always

thought it was because it was a small, dedicated staff that had nothing else in mind but trying to help the people.

Dean, too, was greatly engaged in the new venture. It was he who in the early days taught classes—with energy and conviction—in the "attitude therapy" which was to be an essential feature of Crest's identity.

> Jim Dean was the medical director when I went there. . . . My, he was a dynamo of a man. What he did was to come to Crest to train people in something so new, and he did it beautifully. He was a very small man, but a very decisive one. We used to call him "Little Caesar." And you just had the feeling that he was always in control. And he taught people—you know, attitude therapy. The whole bit. Really a strong leader, I thought, in the hospital.

The strong leaders had enthusiastic followers. The ward staff's involvement and identification with Crest at this beginning period was almost unanimous. Most of the ward staff members were new to mental hospital work; certainly, there were no "bughousers" among them. Most had few preconceptions about the way a hospital should operate.

One aide had begun by being skeptical. He had majored in psychology in a university department which was opposed to psychoanalysis. After a short while at Crest, he found himself becoming "tremendously hopeful."

> It's hard to explain, really . . . you know, how you feel about a place. There are no words to describe it. You saw all this good being done, and you felt you were part of it. It was communicated all the way down from the top to the bottom—from the maintenance man up, and from the medical director on down.

An aide who had applied for a job because of the enthusiasm of some of his friends, was disappointed at first by the condition of the buildings, inside and out—"I thought it was really shabby." But, "After a couple of days, I was amazed at how intimate and comfortable and warm the place was, staffwise; and I thought the relations of the staff with the patients were terrific."

A relatively naïve girl who had worked as an aide at a state hospital described her early response to Crest:

> I don't think I ever had quite an impression like that about a job. I thought it was just fabulous, I really did, and I was very happy. I was so pleased that I had gone out there. I don't know, there was something about it, that I just thought it was a fabulous place, and I agreed with the type of treatment that they were doing, and everyone seemed to be together, to get along so well, the staff and everything. It was just a very pleasant place to work, and everybody was very helpful to each other, to the people who were new and learning.

As new people joined the staff, then, they found themselves in the midst of a congenial group, bound together by its mutual identification with the hospital. The effect of this fellowship and identification—so "intimate and comfortable and warm"—was to influence new members to accept the already existing identity as their own. A somewhat older, more sophisticated aide indicated this process:

> Well, I had heard a lot about the hospital. The people who were working there at that time used to gather together socially, it seemed, every night; and the chief topic of the discussion was the hospital. And they discussed the patients, of course, but they also discussed the hospital's function, the hospital as an organization, as I recall, with great enthusiasm and faith.
>
> The first feeling is that you can't possibly fit in. I had an awful lot of reading to do and lots of things to memorize, and it just seemed like a hopeless task. But it didn't take long before I began to develop the old *esprit de corps* that everybody else had, and I too began to feel that it was a tremendously worthy organization, and that it would grow into one of the finest psychiatric facilities in the country.

A similar experience is described by the recreational therapy director, who had come to Crest from Menningers:

> I just never felt so welcomed in a group, and very quickly got to know people well. I lived alone for the first month I was here, and . . . within a month I was starting to make very good close friends. And by the time I was there three months, I moved into a house with three nurses. . . . Just a close-knit group of people in the hospital, with an interest in everybody's lives . . . everybody was consumed with it—they, their friends—were with this group, and it was hard to know when you were working and when you were playing, because we liked our work, and when we went home, we were so interested that we very frequently discussed the hospital.

Excitement and enthusiasm of the staff, both professional and nonprofessional, and an emphasis on attitude therapy, characterized and identified the hospital at this stage. The staff believed that Crest's therapeutic success was exceptional, and that its total approach to treatment was pioneering and unique. This was by no means valid. The major treatment methods used at Crest at this time were not at all unusual, nor had the original vision been specially radical. Dr. Crawford, in his "Preliminary Proposals" of June, 1950, described the professional's early view of treatment at this ideal hospital.

> A new private psychiatric hospital in the Columbia area should have a small but well equipped unit for the safe detention and active treatment of the occasional hyperactive or definitely suicidal patient. Such a unit should comprise three or four rooms in which patients may be temporarily placed so that they can do no harm to themselves or to others and in which sedative packs and a continuous (sedative) bath tub are available. With such facilities and adequate nursing care, the use of physical restraint apparatus can usually be avoided and, more important, a not inconsiderable proportion of disturbed

patients can recover without having to undergo a "sanity hearing" and legal commitment.

The greatest need, however, is for more adequate means of providing active, relatively short-term care for acutely sick, but not markedly disturbed, psychiatric patients. This means "locked ward" or "closed ward" accommodations, including recreational and occupational therapy facilities.

By "locked ward" facilities, we do not imply that patients are housed in wards or that individual rooms are locked; usually the outside doors of a building or of various units within a building are locked, but with free access on the part of patients to their own rooms and to living and recreation rooms. Within such "locked buildings," patients are usually segregated in terms of sex, severity of symptoms, and, sometimes, age. The bulk of our sanitarium practice consists in persons who require this type of temporary confinement. For some, a brief course of electro-shock or sub-convulsive insulin treatments is indicated—a matter of no more than a few weeks in most instances—after which they are able to begin psychotherapy either as outpatients (coming to the Clinic) or as residents in an "open" section of the sanitarium. Whereas, therefore, we think in terms of a three or four bed unit for very disturbed patients, we must plan for perhaps 35 to 40 beds for the type of patient just described.

There will be an increasing demand for "open ward" beds, i.e., for sanitarium facilities in the more familiar sense of the word, but in a setting that provides physiotherapy, occupational and recreational therapies, and other adjunctive treatment resources not now available in private psychiatric institutions in this area. Such accommodations are needed even now for patients who have partially recovered from a mental illness that initially required protective care and active pharmacological treatment methods, but who no longer require confinement and whose treatment permits a greater freedom of movement. In addition, there will be an increasing volume of patients of the type who never need "locked building" treatment at all, but who do need to get away, temporarily, from a difficult environment and into an active sanitarium treatment program, including psychotherapy.

Not only was the planning fairly conservative, but practice itself during the early days did not seem to warrant the conviction of uniqueness held by Crestites. Dr. Jones says:

> There was a good deal of enthusiasm and idealism about what we were out to do. But in fact I don't think we were doing anything very different than we did at Maple Leaf to begin with.
>
> A large percentage of patients were four to six weeks hospitalizations. There were certain steadies . . . but the turnover was fairly rapid, and quite a bit of ECT was the mainstay.

Dr. Jones added that very few patients were in formal psychotherapy.[1]

All of this seems to indicate that no striking new step in treatment had been taken by the time the hospital was several months old. Yet at the board meeting of September 28, 1950, five days after the hospital opened, Dr. Dean ". . . reported that patients were already responding to the difference in the care they are receiving and that they have developed an *esprit de corps* which corresponds to that of the staff in undertaking a new, exciting adventure."

What seems evident is that although the treatment program was not unique, the atmosphere and spirit of the hospital were special. While a number of factors contributed to this result, the emphasis upon "milieu therapy" was undoubtedly highly significant.

---

[1] Our sampling data indicate that in 1951, 50 per cent of patients received either electric shock or sub-shock insulin treatment; 4 per cent received only psychotherapy. These data, and others referred to later in the text, are based on a sample collected from case history files. The histories were kept in alphabetical order. From an arbitrary starting point, every fifth history was selected.

Underlying the idea of milieu therapy is the conception that all the patient's contacts and experiences possess therapeutic potential. When an individual is in a hospital setting, it is possible for the therapeutic program to be in effect twenty-four hours a day, rather than during one hour of psychotherapy or for the time of an electric shock treatment. The establishment of a milieu therapy program requires that all personnel see their contacts with patients as part of the treatment, that concern be given to the sort of milieu that is especially appropriate therapeutically for each particular patient, and that the whole staff be informed of the general therapeutic plan, and capable of carrying it out.

The hospital staff at Crest, and even the board, responded enthusiastically to the milieu theory. An early board member says that milieu was regarded as "the white horse," other forms of treatment as "the black." Milieu therapy, demanding as it did each individual's conception of himself as important to treatment, led almost everyone at Crest to identify strongly with the institution and its aims, with a resultant high level of dedication.

Attitude therapy, the specific form of milieu therapy that was so central at Crest, was adopted from the Menninger Clinic. This of course was not surprising. Part of the identification of Crest with Menninger's had its roots in the prehistory of the hospital. Drs. Crawford, Clark, Dean, and Jones were Menninger-trained. When new staff members were chosen for important positions, they were almost invariably Menningerites.

The Menninger "Guide to the Order Sheet," and even the Menninger order sheets, were borrowed by Crest and put into use. The "Guide to the Order Sheet" described the attitudes the staff was to adopt toward different kinds of patients.[2] The atti-

---

[2] Definition of Attitide: A habitual reaction in regard to a matter as to reveal an opinion. Note: All attitude therapy is based on friendliness as a basic attitude. *Active Friendliness:* The employee takes the initiative in making friendly gestures, in displaying special interest and thoughtfulness toward the patient. Friendliness can be controlled in amount and degree as shown in the following types of active friendliness: Solicitousness, Extra Attention, Reassurance, Commendation of Proper Verbal Expression, Praise for Acceptable Behavior or Achievement, Companionship, Reward with Companionship. *Passive Friendliness:* The employee should always be available, should maintain his contact with the patient, but never should force his attentions at any time. Wait for the patient to take the initiative. The

tudes were based upon psychodynamic principles; they included various patterns of behavior such as active friendliness, passive friendliness, and kind firmness.

Some examples of the use of attitudes based on dynamic principles are as follows: A depressed patient was seen as turning aggression inward. An attitude of "firm kindness" combined with the use of an extensive compulsive schedule of activities, including menial labor, was pointed toward aiding the patient to direct his aggression outward, to relieve the depression. "Passive friendliness" might be used with a paranoid patient. The point was not to press him too far, but to be prepared to respond to any overture that the patient might make. These orders were to be written; that is, the attitude was to be prescribed by the physician; the expected result was a consistent milieu for the patient which had been determined with therapeutic intent for his particular difficulty.

Attitudes were taught to the Crest staff—nurses, aides, gardeners, occupational and recreational therapists. They guided the staff in a way of behaving which was defined as therapeutic. The emphasis on the importance of a consistent total milieu assigned a significant role in the actual therapy of the patient to each person working at the hospital. Staff members felt that if they did not carry out the attitude they were not doing the therapeutic thing; if they did carry out the attitude, they were helping the patient get well.

In the beginning, as we have noted, Dr. Dean instructed the staff in attitude therapy. Later, however, these classes came under the direction of Ruth Nichols, the new director of nursing services. Mrs. Stark, the first nursing director, had done a satis-

---

employee may at times be firm or severe, but always with a friendly approach. This attitude may safely be adopted when dealing with new patients. *Matter of Fact:* Make no emotional response to a patient's pleas or agitation —though the employee should be friendly. Show no concern over his self-depreciation and do not offer reassurance about his delusions. But employee may still exhibit a friendly interest in the patient's ideas or activities. *Kind Firmness:* Be positive with patient, make invitations definite but friendly and insist the requests be followed. Tell patient—do not ask him. The employee must convey the idea that he means what he says. Requests should be refused in a positive manner that leaves no room for argument.

factory job, but when it was possible to get Miss Nichols, she was hired because of her special qualifications. (Mrs. Stark remained on the staff in a subordinate position.) Ruth Nichols was particularly suited for the Crest position. She had trained at the fountainhead, Menningers; she had worked in a high administrative position at Chestnut Lodge; and the psychoanalytic leaders in Columbia had high personal and professional respect for her. Miss Nichols described her feelings about taking over the classes in attitude therapy:

> One of the things, too, that I think out to be put down is that Jim Dean was the one who really originated attitude therapy there. He held classes for aides and nurses. And I had been away from attitude therapy for a number of years, because I had left Menningers and had not used it; and I felt very insecure about this, because I had forgotten a lot of it; and then also some of the ideas had changed about it. Dick Jones was saying, "You know, you've got to keep on with the classes with nurses and aides, I don't have this kind of time." And I was being expected to teach classes, which I did—but feeling very insecure about the attitude therapy, mainly because I had some doubts about it myself, and also not remembering a lot of things—and it was only from relearning from Jim of the theoretical background to be able to explain to people about . . . and I wrote to Menningers, got their old booklet on it and a number of things, so I could be a little more sure of myself.

Dr. Dean spent only five hours a week at the hospital, and devoted this time almost totally to staff training. Dr. Jones was in charge of the treatment program, under Dr. Clark's guidance. He says:

> Now Jim Dean and I were very close friends, and I always felt that I was in charge of the hospital and he was kind of a nominal medical director; but I'm not sure he felt that way. I mean, we worked well together, and I don't think there was any supervisory function. I think Jim had the liaison with the board; and then we started

> having staff conferences at the hospital; and Jim would attend those—and actually I think frequently I wouldn't be able to, or I was in analysis—and in a way he was switching off in certain things for me, to give me relief.

Jones spent considerably more time at the hospital than Dean and, as noted earlier, lived nearby and was available evenings and weekends. However, he had half-time duties at the Columbia Clinic. Miss Nichols reports that she began to carry more of the responsibility for the treatment program.

> This was the beginning of where I think I began to take over really much more; and Dick was saying, "Now Ruth you—" (I would call up and say, so-and-so is about to leave the hospital) "would you go in and talk to her, and you explain this, and this," and he'd be downtown and, "you keep her there." Well, more and more Dick relied on all of us to make decisions with patients, and let him know. And this was a period in which I think in many respects I ran the hospital much more than Dick did.

It is doubtful that this shift in responsibility would have come about had the head nurse not been the person she was. We have outlined her background, but her manifest traits and the drives behind them were primarily at work in the role she came to play in the hospital. That this slim, black-haired, intense woman had special qualities of leadership seems beyond question. Some indication of these qualities and how they functioned at Crest is given in the statements below.

> There wasn't anybody who was a significantly powerful personality in the form of a director, as opposed to the head nurse.

> She worked constantly in an effort to improve the function of the whole hospital.

> Ruth . . . would listen to anybody, anytime.

> Aides adored Ruth—Ruth was their everything, because she liked her aides, and she taught them, and she really cared about them. Ruth was the greatest.

. . . I have a feeling that there is quite a definite need in herself to have the various members of the nursing department particularly dependent upon her in some way—as though she had a need for them to come to her with personal problems. . . . In many ways she must have been very capable, and provided a great deal of strength.

. . . as one of the professional staff—felt she was senior to me; and I think that had some reality to it, in that I had sessions with her which were essentially her supervising me in management. I think Ruth's attitude was sort of maternal and protective—I mean, bossy in a nice way—and she looked upon me as some sort of fellow who had lots to learn. . . . It was sort of a strange situation, with the head nurse being sort of second in command. But after all she was really somebody that had more experience than everybody else put together, really. She certainly seemed to know how to get along with patients, to be able to relate to them and get next to them, and make them feel a little better. I think that my talking with her was probably helpful to me in treating patients. . . . She was some support.

I have the feeling that . . . she really ran Crest; and I don't know what role the doctors had, nor do I know how they resolved having a woman, a nurse, pretty much control the situation. . . . But apparently she must have done it so skillfully.

We have included the foregoing views because they do more than illustrate that Miss Nichols was the sort of personality ready, willing, and able to exercise power. They also reveal the situation in which this power was exercised, a situation which further developed Crest's emergent identity.

Drs. Dean and Jones often were not available, and much authority devolved upon Miss Nichols. Under her leadership, the nursing staff gained increased autonomy and influence over the treatment program. The emphasis upon attitude therapy permitted the nonprofessional people to see themselves as legitimately taking a great deal of responsibility for patients. Given the milieu philosophy, it seemed quite natural to the staff that personnel at all levels should be involved in decisions about treatment. The recreational therapist says of this period:

> It was my feeling that we really worked together and respected each other's judgment. I think one of the most notable things about it was the aides' and nurses', everybody's feeling of freedom to suggest what they thought should be done, how something should be handled—really, the doctor's dependence upon the judgment of the people like the aides, OT, RT. . . .

Dr. Jones helps to round out the picture with these recollections:

> There was an awful lot of informal discussion between me—and between Dean, too—and the nurses and aides. They would attend the conferences, of course, but in addition to that, there was a lot of attention given to the activity-prescription and the writing of the prescription, and the elaborating of it to the head nurse.

There were at this time very few complaints about problems of status, about who should take what function, about who had the right to do what—in short, about the hierarchical structure within the hospital. The people at the top seemed to be doing what was expected of them: they were respected as effective, and as helpful to the people further down the line. The professional people, for their part, had the highest regard for the ward staff. The minutes of the Board of Trustees state:

> Sanitarium personnel are working smoothly, and Dr. Dean feels he has a "good crew."
>
> Dr. Dean commented briefly upon the continued high quality and excellent work of the nursing and attendant staffs at the Sanitarium.

The "family spirit" of the staff was felt to be a good and beneficial thing.

The aides and nurses, then, were treated as though they were capable of running the hospital. And it was not long before they appeared to be doing precisely that. The power and autonomy of the nursing staff are illustrated by an account of what happened when "outside" psychiatrists treated patients at Crest. The story of these "outsiders" deserves to be told in detail.

The issue first arose in the prehistory of the hospital when Crawford and Clark were trying to explain to the board the need to have a consistent treatment situation at Crest. This was an attempt to ease the concern of Mr. Bell who had actively expressed his desire that the hospital be a community hospital and open to psychiatrists other than the psychoanalytic Columbia Clinic group. In the *modus vivendi* that was reached later there was an agreement that the Columbia Clinic group would control the therapeutic atmosphere at the hospital. At the same time the clinic representatives went along, ambivalently, with the involvement of some other psychiatrists, in an attempt to please or appease Mr. Bell. However, they did not suppress their discontent with the arrangement. This discontent was communicated to the nursing staff which, flexing their newfound muscles, dealt with the outsiders in a way which seemed both to solidify their own position and to fulfill the wishes of their psychoanalytic parents.

The story of the "outsiders" begins with Dr. Oliver Grayford, in November, 1950, shortly after the hospital opened. Dr. Grayford, while not psychoanalytically oriented, was in analysis at the time. He was a local product, a psychiatrist with a large hospital practice which he treated largely with organic means. He first appears in the picture in a discussion at the Board of Trustees meeting of November 23, 1950.

> The secretary also reported a conversation with Dr. Oliver A. Grayford of Columbia in which the secretary told Dr. Grayford that while it was the temporary policy of the Foundation to select its medical staff from the Columbia Clinic, it was the intention of the Foundation to add other psychiatrists to the staff as soon as the organizational phase of the Sanitarium was over and as soon as facilities permitted. Dr. Grayford had assured the secretary of his deep interest in the purposes of the Sanitar-

ium, of his understanding of the temporary policies of the Foundation with respect to medical staff, and of his personal desire to be associated with the Sanitarium as soon as facilities are available for the larger medical staff.

There ensued a discussion as to the feasibility of adding Dr. Oliver A. Grayford to the staff of the Crest Sanitarium in the near future, and the consensus was that this could be done provided Dr. Grayford did not wish at this time to hospitalize all of his sanitarium patients at the Crest Sanitarium. Dr. Barclay and Dr. Clark were requested to interview Dr. Grayford in an attempt to reach mutually satisfactory agreement looking forward to Dr. Grayford's being appointed to the staff. Upon motion duly made by Mr. Bell, seconded by Mrs. Mahoney, it was Resolved that the Trustees' Committee on Professional Staff proceed to designate the medical staff of the Crest Foundation Sanitarium and to submit a report at the next meeting of the Trustees.

At the following meeting, on December 28, 1950, the professional committee of the board made recommendations of appointments to the Crest visiting staff: Drs. Jones, Hagen, Carpenter, Harris, Clark, and Towse, all of the Columbia Clinic, and Dr. Oliver A. Grayford.

In a conversation with Dr. Grayford, he recognized the limitations of bed space at the Sanitarium, and he expressed a willingness to cooperate fully in our efforts to carry out attitude and other therapies as have been expressed in the philosophy of the Sanitarium.

Then, on January 25, 1951, the minutes stated:

Mr. Johnson reported that Dr. Oliver A. Grayford, recently appointed to the staff, now has two patients at the hospital and indicates that he is well satisfied with its facilities and with the cooperation of the staff.

The formal organization of the attending medical staff was not completed until July 5, 1952, a year and a half later. Dr. Grayford, although he did not attend that meeting, was appointed chairman of the Crest medical advisory committee. Actually, he never attended a meeting of the formal attending staff; he was always listed as an unexcused absence. On June 13, 1953, at a meeting of the attending staff, Dr. Clark informed the group this was the time the board should have recommendations for reappointment; he moved that all consultants be reappointed and that all members of the active staff at present—with the exception of Dr. Grayford—be appointed. This was unanimously approved. "After some discussion it was felt that Dr. Grayford should be told by the Board of Trustees that the Staff had not recommended his reappointment."

At its meeting of June 26, 1953, the board heard an oral report from its professional committee. The committee had consulted by telephone with Dr. Phelan, the new Crest chief of staff. Roger Phelan, short, somewhat dumpy, but very vigorous, was a senior psychoanalyst who had recently joined the Columbia Clinic staff after having served for many years on the senior staff of the Menninger Foundation. He had considerable hospital experience, and took over the chief consultant position which Dr. Clark had held from Crest's beginning. The minutes stated that:

> ... the Active Medical Staff be reappointed with the exception of Dr. Oliver A. Grayford—for one year.
>
> It was the opinion expressed in Dr. Phelan's letter that the Hospital Staff felt that Dr. Grayford should be informed by the Board of Trustees that his reappointment had not been recommended by the Staff. It was felt by some of the Crest Staff that he should be told that we had previously discussed the matter of Associate Medical Staff membership and had decided against this because it would go against the basic philosophy of Crest Sanitarium in that the active working together of all the staff is an essential feature of the function. Dr. Grayford had sent a letter to the staff meeting, which was read in his absence and in which he suggested that possibly, if he was appointed to the Associate Medical Staff, this might be a way out of the dilemma. Inasmuch as such an Associate membership (which by the way does not exist at the

present time) would mean that he could admit patients but would have no opportunity to be indoctrinated in Crest Foundation Sanitarium philosophy—this was the chief reason why the Associate Staff membership category was not included in the By-Laws of the Constitution of the Crest Staff. Dr. Phelan suggested that perhaps Dr. Grayford could be told that at a later date he could re-apply without prejudice if he wished to take an active part in the work of the Sanitarium staff.

The professional committee unanimously had accepted these recommendations. The board approved, and the secretary was instructed to inform Dr. Grayford.

Dr. Grayford's response to his experiences at Crest was not positive. He found the personnel at Crest rule-and-regulation conscious; it is his opinion that adherence to rules and regula-tions is not the best way to help a patient. Some of his recom-mendations were not accepted by the hospital staff; his orders were followed reluctantly. Dr. Grayford felt that the manner in which his prescriptions and orders were carried out made a sig-nificant difference in their effectiveness. He became dissatisfied with the arrangement, and gradually "dropped out."

Dr. Grayford stated that the Board of Trustees was aware that he had a different therapeutic orientation.

(Did they have the impression then that the hospital was eclectic? How aware were they of the fact that it was gen-erally psychoanalytic in orientation?) I think they thought that if I was there, that I would sort of keep it clean; I think that as much as anything it was a personal opinion that it was a . . . I mean they didn't know what "analytically oriented" meant, but they thought that they didn't want a closed shop, this was the idea. (So it was not so much the analytic orientation as opening it up to other people?) Yes, in other words, they didn't feel that they wanted to be—that they wanted to be contrib-uting to the Columbia Clinic; and as far as they were concerned, as long as Sid Clark and Tom Crawford were the only ones there, then this was just the Columbia

Clinic's hospital; but if they bring in an outlander like
. . . Harris was even with the Columbia Clinic at that
time . . . so I was strictly the representative of the
public.

Two other psychiatrists also sent patients to Crest. One, Dr.
Gerald Harris, who at one time had been analytically oriented
but had become separated from the analytic idea, stated:

To give you an example: one of the things I questioned
at Menningers; there was a concept of the therapist and
of another doctor who handled administrative duties
. . . and the patient went to the administrator, who
told him what he could or couldn't do, and this was not
in the province of the therapist. My feeling was that the
therapist would be the one who would know better than
anyone else, and—if it should be possible—to both do the
therapy and the administration at the same time.

(There was criticism on the part of the staff that you
wanted to manage your patients?) That's right. (How
was this reacted to by the people out at the hospital?)
Well, I had the feeling that they didn't like it, or that
they [thought they] could do it better than I could.
(Does this mean that they didn't follow through on the
orders?) Well, I wouldn't say that they didn't, but let's
say without enthusiasm. (Was this mostly the medical
staff or the nursing staff that did this?) Both. Because the
staff out there was sold pretty much on their way of seeing things. They had conferences with the nursing staff
and attendants.

Dr. Harris saw a basic philosophical difference between himself and the people at Crest; he was beginning to doubt the
analytic approach, while they, he felt, were sticking to orthodoxy.
Within the framework of Crest's philosophy, the personnel carried the job out adequately. However:

The patient [at Crest] became an object rather than
another human being. For example, the tone of the staff
conferences as they talked about a patient, or even more

so when they would sit around the lunch table. And if they talk about them, this patient and that patient—particularly if they talk about what goes on in the patient's unconscious—"I'm aware of it; he's not"—and as they laugh about it, well we all do at times. I don't mean you can't laugh about it once in awhile, but there is an implied superiority in it . . . we really know better than anyone.

Dr. Harris went on to say, "When I differed, I was looked down upon." He also said, "I couldn't feel that for the money spent the patients were getting what they were—enough for it."

Dr. Waller, a Menninger-trained psychiatrist whose views about hospital treatment were not those emphasized by the psychoanalytic group, also brought patients to Crest. His rather eloquent expression follows:

It was peculiar to go on the ward there. I never had a feeling that there was any rapport between the staff and the patients, especially when I'd go on the acute ward. On the acute ward they had several little cubicles; and the attendants would be in these cubicles drinking coffee and smoking cigarettes, and every now and then they would sort of go out and make a kind of a foray on the patient, and then they would retreat. It was sort of—I don't know—kind of an animal-like, almost animosity between the patients and the attendants there, the nurses. Patients were often pushed around despite all the ideas about nonviolence or tender loving care and so on; you had a feeling that the attendants didn't know how to carry out the orders, and they were given things to do that were beyond their scope and beyond their understanding. It is always a moot question how much attitude therapy does, how much milieu therapy does, how much all the recreational and other therapy can accomplish, anyway; but this seemed to be an important part, a very, very big and large and important part of the entire total push program, total therapy program. You had these disturbed people who didn't know what they were doing, trying to do it, and I think it made things worse, very often.

I remember one time I had a patient there who was a life-long schizophrenic person, who had treatment with several different physicians here—finally brought her at one time to me and I admitted her to Crest. She began to make some progress there, and I had her . . . on the back ward, acute ward, for quite awhile; and I was giving her fairly deep, but not shock insulin—call it sub-coma insulin. And every time I'd come on the ward, I had such a funny feeling. I had a feeling as if I wasn't accepted as a doctor, I wasn't accepted as one of the staff—capital, T H E, staff—I was an interloper, or outsider, or something or other. And I remember talking to Jones, and I said to Dick I have this funny feeling, I wonder if I'm getting a little paranoid because I come on the ward and I'm treated in such a peculiar way. Ordinarily you walk into a hospital, the nurses are supposed by tradition to stand up, greet the doctor, no one with hands in his pockets, certain decorum and so on. The doctor is supposed to be a pretty important figure whether he knows his business or not—you respect the uniform but not the guy in the uniform. When I came here, the attendants and the nurses would disappear, or they would not say good morning, or they wouldn't give a decent report about the patient. I'd read these great, long, voluminous accounts in the record about what everybody is doing, and so on; and it wasn't too meaningful. There was one nurse there, I felt that she was really quite looney and very, very aggressive. So I came on the ward one day, and the patient hadn't gotten her insulin treatment. I said, "Well how come?" Well, she told me that she decided the patient didn't need insulin anymore. Well, I talked to Jones about this, and he said . . . he had the feeling sometimes, as director or assistant director, of the same kind of treatment. So I thought to myself, well, either I'm going to treat the patient, or the nurse is going to treat the patient; either I'm going to treat the patient, or all these people out at Crest are going to treat the patient. I think they are wrecking the therapy and wrecking this woman's chances. So I called the family and told them I don't think the patient is going to do well at Crest, and I want to transfer her to Evergreen; and this I did. And to my good fortune, and to the patient's good fortune, the patient made very, very good treatment progress, the treatment was successful, and she went into remission, and as far as I know she's been in remission ever since.

I remember giving shock treatment to one or two patients out there, and they had a shock machine there, but the attitude that if you're giving shock treatment—I don't know—this is some sort of quackery, or buggery, or something is going on.

If you tried to use these other treatments they didn't approve of it—I don't know who didn't approve of it, whether the Consulting Staff didn't or the administration didn't or the nurses didn't or the attendants didn't. But I found as a doctor in charge of a patient—the patient being entrusted to me by the family or the patient's own will—I couldn't do what I wanted to do, because this was not accepted. And these treatments were not treatments that were generally frowned on by psychiatrists, so it wasn't as if I were coming in with monkey gland therapy, you know. So after this business with this patient, I don't think I admitted any more patients there.

I thought everybody was [crazy] there, where the nurses would tell the doctor what to do, and the nurses kind of cracked, and Jones himself tells me he's not—he's director or assistant director, or was—and when he was not in control of the hospital, but these other people were pushing him around. So what's the point of my admitting patients there? It costs a heck of a lot of money to go there; they are not getting good treatment; they are not getting well; the rate of recovery was not as good as I thought I was getting at Evergreen; it cost the patient less; I felt a hell of a lot more comfortable at Evergreen— so why have to put up with all this sort of stuff?

The view of the staff at Crest was somewhat different. Miss Nichols discussed this period:

> We would have six or eight doctors coming out there, who would send patients out and be directly responsible for them. If they had psychotherapy, they had to go into town; but if they didn't, the doctors came out and saw them. The doctors wrote all the orders, and this was chaotic; this was a real problem that Dick [Jones] and I had. For instance, there would be rules, like all patients on shock could not have ground privileges for so many days, because Dick felt that they would wander off and get lost—this kind of thing . . . [all] patients . . . had their mail censored. When the new doctors started coming out, they did not adhere to this. . . . Everybody was quite perturbed, because there would be one patient who was saying, well, if she doesn't have to have her mail censored, why do I have to have mine; if he can have privileges, why can't I? Visitors were handled differently, weekend passes were handled differently. And so I remember finally Dick saying, "Ruth, you sit down and write out a bunch of regulations that we have, that we have established—write down these things and we will have them mimeographed and sent to every doctor who is sending patients out here," which he did. There was a lot of discussion about whether this should be or shouldn't be, and the Board I guess at that time was feeling that all doctors should have a part in this, the hospital is growing, etc. . . .
>
> And then we went through that period with Waller . . . and the kids were really mad at him about the way he gave electric shock therapy, because he stepped on the button instead of pressing it with his finger; and they called me in one day, and that day he picked it up off the floor; and from that day on he didn't come out anymore.

It is significant that these "outsiders" did not treat patients differently than patients were being treated at Crest. As noted earlier, the major form of specific treatment at Crest was physical; and few patients were receiving individual psychotherapy. Thus, it was not the use of physical treatment that caused the conflict with the ward staff, but, rather, the indifference toward milieu exhibited by the "outside" psychiatrists. From the ward staff's viewpoint, the physicians seemed to be under the "grand illusion" that they and the treatment they offered might actually have something to do with helping the patient. It was clear to the ward staff that these physicians saw themselves as primarily responsible for the patient. The ward staff regarded this view as invalid. They considered themselves the major treatment source. Milieu, after all, was the theme; attitude therapy could be counted on to help the patient. It was the lack of appreciation of, and involvement with, this theme, the lack of respect for the staff working directly with patients, which seemed to bring about the intense conflict.

Dr. Jones said:

> I'm not clear about the time sequence here but I know at some point there was a drive to let outside doctors come in and it was tried particularly with Waller and I think Harris, and to draw them in and to sell them on the idea that they could come in there and treat their patients, manage them, and that I would just be the resident around there and wouldn't get in their hair or interfere, would take advice and so on. And particularly with Waller, who was Menninger trained, and should have the same orientation, it was a dismal failure, not from my point of view, but from the relationship between the outside doctor and Ruth or the nursing staff; they just didn't talk the same language, and it just didn't work. (The same was true of Dr. Harris?) Yes, well, that I would expect; he didn't have the Menninger training that Waller did. And I am not sure it was a matter of training, but it just would not work at all . . . Harris had people at Hilltop that he seemed to get along fine with, but he couldn't get along fine with the Crest set-up. And it was simply that the nurses were used to working with me or . . . whoever it was. And personally I feel that Ruth . . . in a way treated patients; they knew quite a bit

about what the patient's needs were; they would ask me for the order they wanted and I would modify it or direct them in it. But the thing wouldn't have worked at all without a strong head nurse, which we had all the time.

What happened to the "outsiders" was a consequence of a number of forces which made up the "field" at Crest during these early days. But the final result clearly strengthened the feeling of power and autonomy of the hospital nursing and aide staff. The professional people, both at the hospital and at the Columbia Clinic, were ambivalent in dealing with their colleagues. Some were acutely concerned with accommodating Mr. Bell. But the ward staff were not ambivalent; and with the vaguely expressed support of the professional people involved, they pushed out the "outsiders." Again, the leadership of Miss Nichols must be emphasized. She was dedicated to milieu and attitude therapy; and she was in authority most of the time: "Miss Nichols' office was right there, and I don't think many people had too many qualms as long as she was on the grounds."

The "outsiders" stated again and again that they did not see Crest as a particularly effective hospital. All of them believed that they obtained better results in treating their patients elsewhere. On the other hand, the evidence is overwhelming that Crestites found support for the positive identity of the hospital in their perception of the results of its treatment program. Dr. Crawford said:

> In my opinion Crest best fulfilled its purposes and philosophy in the period . . . under the part-time medical directors. . . . [Then] there was a strong Menninger tradition at Crest, but it was geared to the realities of the new hospital, the new environment and the type of patients referred to it. . . . So far as I know, there was general satisfaction with the pioneer work of the early, part-time medical directors.

An aide said:

> I think that the ward staff felt that they were very effective. I did. I felt—and everybody that I talked to; and you

know people who knew each other well—we would talk about it, and I didn't feel any discontent . . . because everybody always spoke of Crest, and believed that it was the thing.

Another aide—a housewife who had originally objected to having an "insane asylum" in the neighborhood—came to have these views:

> I thought it was very good. Of course, not having any experience at all—this type of experience, with mentally disturbed people—everything was quite new to me and quite remarkable. And I was quite surprised as to how sick some of these people were, and yet the staff was able to manage and treat them with a considerable amount of effectiveness no matter how disturbed they were, really how crazy they were, just amazed me. And it was all in what you said—your attitude. The work itself was important, not in what it was doing for us or what we were getting but what it was doing for these people. It was just miraculous, it just amazed me. Every now and then I think of certain patients that were literally crawling on the floor. Six months later they would go home and take care of their children and be a member of the community. And this is what we were doing, you know. And otherwise there were a lot of people that were working there that could have gotten more money elsewhere. It wasn't the wages that kept people on at Crest, at least, at my level it wasn't.

The recreational therapist said:

> It was my feeling that the patients really had the feeling of being home there, that they did very well. There was lots of warmth and attachments to the hospital, and patients came in disturbed, and were able to relax. We weren't anxious. Everybody was pretty comfortable, the patients included.

During this period Crest grew in all realms: in physical facilities, in program, in patient census, and in staff. About a year after the hospital opened, in December, 1951, a new "wing for disturbed and noisy patients" was completed. When it opened, it was filled from a waiting list of patients. A year later, in January, 1953, the patient census and revenue were the highest since Crest's opening. In May, 1953, Crest was expanded, through remodeling, to facilities for thirty-five patients. The educational and training program also developed. By December, 1951, advanced students in psychiatric nursing, from the local university, were being trained at Crest. And in February, 1953, a psychiatric resident took up duties at Crest.

The most important aspect of this growth process was in the quantity and quality of staff. A month after the hospital opened, in October, 1950, a third psychiatric nurse was added. On June 1, 1951, the assistant director of recreational therapy at the Menninger Foundation was hired to be director of recreational therapy at Crest. Ruth Nichols joined the staff in July, 1951. Finally, late in 1952, the board decided to hire a full-time professional staff. In August, 1953, the board approved two applications for permanent, full-time jobs, from Leonard Paulson, as clinical psychologist, and from Dr. George Dunn as assistant medical director.

Paulson had been trained as a clinical psychologist in Topeka, as part of the first group in the Veterans Administration clinical psychology training program under the joint control and direction of Kansas University, Winter Veterans Administration Hospital, and the Menninger Foundation. He had not yet received his Ph.D., needing only to defend his thesis. Dunn, too, was Menninger-trained, having completed three years of psychiatric residency in Topeka. Both were young and enthusiastic; and they were friends. Paulson arrived at Crest—the first full-time professional employee—in September, 1953. Dunn arrived on New Year's Day, 1954. With the new staff a new epoch began for Crest.

CHAPTER FOUR

Autonomy– A Full-Time Director

We have described the early development of Crest as an institution, its actual physical growth, and the establishment of a strong identity. We have seen, too, that conflicts existed between some members of the Board of Trustees and some of the psychoanalysts concerned with the direction of Crest. By late 1952, and through 1953, the appointment of a full-time medical director and a full-time staff had become the aim of all parties. These appointments seemed to be reasonable steps to insure the continuing growth of Crest, and were seen also as the vehicle for the solution of the conflicts and problems that existed between and within the groups and individuals intimately involved with Crest. The appointment of a full-time medical director took center stage.

Mr. Bell, on the board, wished Crest to become independent of the Columbia Clinic and to be more community oriented. He believed the appointment of a medical director would provide the means for getting "rid of the Columbia Clinic."

The Columbia Clinic professionals wished to see Mr. Bell's power diminished in order that Crest might reach toward the highest possible professional standards. Thus, they too, supported the wish for a medical director. As early as December, 1952, at a special meeting of the board, Dr. Crawford stated:

> . . . on behalf of the partners of the Columbia Clinic that the Clinic was ready to withdraw from active treatment of patients at the Sanitarium as soon as the Foundation could employ a competent full-time medical director and provide him with adequate assistance. Dr. Crawford estimated that the monies collected by the Clinic from the treatment of its patients at the Sanitarium would, if collected by the Sanitarium on behalf of the Foundation, more than pay for the salary of a full-time medical director, and of a psychiatric resident or younger psychiatrist associated with him. Dr. Crawford pointed out that the Clinic would be in considerable measure compensated for such a move by having Drs. Daniel [who had replaced Dr. Dean as part-time medical director] and Jones full time at the Clinic. However this may be, the Clinic is taking the position that this is the time for the Sanitarium to become more autonomous. The Clinic will be glad to assist the Foundation in its search for a medical director and will continue to give every assistance possible as consultants to the Board and to the Sanitarium staff.

The hospital staff wanted the continued growth of the hospital and the continued development of its identity. Ruth Nichols, a guest at the board meeting of July, 1953, represented the hospital staff. She spoke to the board and "under-scored the need for a full-time medical director." The minutes stated:

> She is convinced that someone must be there more of the time in order effectively to coordinate the work of the staff, to provide leadership, to take care of a myriad of administrative details, and to assist adequately with teaching. She pointed out that the medical staff is providing one class now as compared to four a year ago. She believes that the appointment of a full-time director will greatly strengthen all aspects of medical administration and patient care at the hospital.

All, then, wished to see Crest autonomous—that is, self-governing, free from outside control—although all did not agree as to what "outside control" should be eliminated. Thus, despite the apparent unanimity of aim, the medical directorship was ensnared in the existing conflicts among Crest's leadership.

In July of 1953, Mr. Bell was reported as being concerned when Dr. Grayford was dropped from the medical staff and it was reported that he was eager for Crest to have its own medical director. The board then, at the July, 1953, meeting, passed a curious motion: "Resolved that prior to the professional committee committing itself to the selection of a medical director, Mr. Jonathan Bell be fully informed of any candidate's qualifications." At this time Mr. Bell was ill and was not attending board meetings. His influence nonetheless remained great, as the unusual character of this resolution attests. Apparently it struck even Mr. Bell as unusual: a few months later, the board president reported that Bell had requested that this resolution not be interpreted as conferring any special status on him, and that he be considered rather on a par with any other members of the board.

Not only the board deferred to Mr. Bell. These are the statements of senior members of the hospital staff, reporting on their visits to Mr. Bell's sickbed during this period:

> I was going to see him every month or so and inform him how things were going. . . . Bell probably was working on me as he worked on everyone else to control the situation. . . . I guess he was the most influential member on the Board.

> I was being sent to see Mr. Bell on little visits and this kind of thing, and I never knew whether Martin Johnson sent me to do this or the doctors, but I was always having to run up and see him and let him know how things were going, this was the idea. He was going to give us some money someday and when other people didn't have time, I could go and visit him, because he was ill in his home, and I used to be ushered into the library and sit and wait

for him, and he toddled out and we discussed the state of affairs.

He was domineering, he wanted a report every week regarding his relative, he wanted to prescribe treatment concerning the Bible or not having the Bible or she should go to bed at 10:00 or at 9:45. Whether there was anything to report or not, he wanted a report. I felt somewhat in a position of being a lackey, of having to go out to Mr. Bell's house and sit in his library and report to Mr. Bell.

By the fall of 1953, this battle for power reached a climax, revealed in the minutes for the November 27 meeting of the Board of Trustees:

> The Chairman of the Professional Committee, Dr. Barclay, read the minutes of the meeting of that Committee held on November 16, 1953, and attended by him, Mr. Britt, and Dr. Clark. These minutes have been considered by the Executive Committee on November 20, 1953, with the recommendation that they be presented to the Board of Trustees. The following is the complete draft of the Professional Committee's report:
>
>> "Letters addressed to the Professional Committee from Dr. R. Phelan, Chief of Staff of Crest Sanitarium; Dr. Philip Daniel, Medical Director of Crest Sanitarium; Miss Ruth Nichols, Director of Nurses at Crest Sanitarium; and Mr. Martin Johnson, Hospital Administrator, were read and discussed. It was unanimously recognized after discussion that a critical condition exists at the Sanitarium in the form of deterioration of group morale, most of this stemming from lack of confidence in the Board of Trustees as a group to satisfactorily support the Foundation financially. While it was recognized that the very urgent need for a medical director to serve full time is the immediate need of the Sanitarium, it was unanimously agreed that no application for medical director would be considered past

the point of approving or disapproving such appli-
cant's professional qualifications and suitability for the
position until all money held under second mortgage
had been converted to gifts to the Foundation. Specifically referred to were the $25,000 second mortgage
held by Mr. Bell [who had earlier made a gift of
$15,000 of his original $40,000 pledge] and the $10,000
mortgage held by the George Britt Fund.

"More specifically, the four letters noted above described lowered standards of patient care, lowered
standards of training for a resident physician, considerable dissatisfaction on the part of the Hospital Administrator because of lack of consistent financial support on the part of the Board of Trustees as a whole
and the recurring necessity on his part of having to go
to one member of the Board for financial assistance in
financial crises.

"The Professional Committee is unwilling to recommend that a medical director be hired until the second
mortgages are either completely paid off or converted
to gifts, until the Board of Trustees as a group assumes
full financial affairs of the Foundation. The Professional Committee feels that a full-time medical director with the proper qualifications could correct the
lowered group morale at the Sanitarium and reverse
the present trend of lowered efficiency with relatively
little difficulty.

"Specifically, then, the Professional Committee recommends to the Executive Committee:

"1. That Mr. Jonathan Bell be approached and urged
to convert the second mortgage held by him of $25,000
to a gift to the Foundation within the next ten days if
at all possible. (Mr. Britt gave full assurance that his
$10,000 would be converted to a gift when the above is
consummated.)

"2. That if and when the second mortgages are converted to gifts to the Foundation, Dr. Mark J. Travers,
at the present time on the staff of the Topeka State

Hospital, Topeka, Kansas, be seriously considered for the position of medical director of the Crest Foundation Sanitarium. The Professional Committee approves Dr. Travers' qualifications for the position. . . . "3. It is recommended to the Executive Committee that the above situation warrants consideration within the next few days."

Following the reading of the Professional Committee's report the letters from Dr. Phelan, Mr. Johnson, Dr. Daniel and Miss Nichols referred to in the report, were read in full. There followed an extended discussion of these letters and of the Professional Committee's report.

It was evident that the anti-Bell forces had joined together in an attempt to separate Bell from his source of power. These forces grasped Bell's special desire for a medical director as the lever which could force him to donate his money. In effect, they proposed a bargain: the professionals would carry out their functions of evaluating, recommending, and supporting a medical director—which Mr. Bell desired to obtain independence from the Columbia Clinic—only if and when Mr. Bell donated his money, thus minimizing his personal power.

That the anti-Bell group was determined is indicated by the unequivocal and undiplomatic tone of the resolution adopted by the Board at that meeting:

RESOLVED that whereas the report of the Professional Committee indicates that a critical condition exists among the professional staff at the Sanitarium, whereas the Committee also recommends that this condition could best be remedied by the appointment of a full-time medical director; whereas the Committee reports that it is unwilling to recommend the appointment of any full-time medical director until all money loaned to the Foundation by members of the Board of Trustees is either converted to gifts or repaid; whereas the Committee feels it is highly unlikely that a satisfactory candidate for the position of full-time medical director will apply for such position until the above-noted internal financial situation within the Board of Trustees is resolved; and whereas the money now on loan to the Foundation by members of the Board of Trustees, originally intended as a gift, constitutes (a) a destructive influence on the efficiency and group morale of the Board of Trustees, (b) a serious obstacle to the successful search for a full-time medical director, and (c) an opportunity for one of the Board to exercise a de facto control over financial and at times professional policies of the Foundation, BE IT RESOLVED that the Board of Trustees of Crest Foundation will (1) bring all efforts to bear to induce members of the Board of Trustees now loaning money to the Foundation to convert this money to gifts to the Foundation; (2) or failing this, will endeavor to repay these loans by obtaining other pledges; and (3) will appoint a medical director only after such action is successfully completed; (4) that the Board of Trustees regards the loaning of money to the Foundation by members of the Board of Trustees as unsound in principle in a nonprofit organization. And finally, the implementing of this motion be the immediate and continued duty of the President and Executive Committee.

The meeting was continued two weeks later, on December 11, 1953. As can be seen, much had happened in the interim. The minutes read:

There ensued a lengthy discussion of the over-all financial position of the Foundation and of the apparent impasse within the Board of Trustees. After a thorough exchange of views, it appeared to be the consensus that the existence of a second mortgage is less of an impediment to constructive action on the part of the Board than had hitherto been assumed and that a much more satisfactory working arrangement between the Board and the hospital administration could be effected by making the Hospital Administrator directly and fully responsible to the Finance Committee of the Board.

In the light of other aspects of the discussion, it appeared also that the Board's action on November 27, 1953, contained in the resolution offered by Dr. Clark, was conceived in haste and incomplete in its interpretation of the situation confronting the Board. In view of this, on motion of Dr. Crawford, seconded by Mr. Roberts, it was

"RESOLVED to rescind the resolution offered by Dr. Clark and passed by the Board on November 27, 1953, and to request the president to appoint a committee to redraft the resolution for resubmission to the Board at its next regular meeting."

Following this clear-cut (although, as will be seen, temporary) victory for Mr. Bell, his wishes seemed to be carried out thoroughly in the next few months. On December 21, 1953, the professional committee recommended Dr. Irving Davidson for the position of medical director. A communication, which was read to the board, ends as follows:

Following our investigation and our conversations with him, the Professional Committee considers his professional and personal qualifications of an exceptionally high order and on this basis recommends his appointment as medical director of the Crest Foundation.

At the next board meeting, in January, 1954,

The President, Mr. Blair, then presented to the Board the Executive Committee's recommendations that the financial plan drawn up for the Columbia Clinic's withdrawal from administrative responsibilities and direct patient care at the Sanitarium be adopted. Under the recommended plan, the Columbia Clinic will collect all income from the medical supervision of patients at Crest during the first six months of 1954 and in return for this will assume financial responsibility for salaries and other administrative costs up to the sum of $12,075.00. After discussion of the details of this plan, upon motion of Mr. Bell, seconded by Mrs. Hagen, it was

"RESOLVED that the Executive Committee's recommendation for the financial aspects of the Columbia Clinic's withdrawal from administrative duties and the active care of patients at Crest Sanitarium be adopted."

Thus, immediately upon the appointment of Dr. Davidson as a full-time medical director, formal proceedings were begun to separate the Columbia Clinic and the Crest Foundation. This was what Mr. Bell had wished. Moreover, he was "pleased" by the appointment of Davidson. And yet, he now made a new ploy with regard to his major area of strength: his money.

On April 24, 1953, Bell's will had stated that the mortgage of $40,000 held on the Crest Foundation would upon his death be given directly to Crest. On March 3, 1954, when Dr. Davidson arrived, a codicil to the will changed this. As noted earlier, in the interim Bell had given $15,000 of the $40,000 mortgage as a gift, and the codicil stated that the remaining $25,000 would go to Crest not before the two years following his death. A qualification was added, stating that his trustees would pass judgment as to whether the money should go to Crest. This judgment should depend upon whether in the opinion of the majority, Crest's services were being rendered for the benefit of the "community as a whole and not for the material or monetary advantage of any single individual or group, and that said institution is an autonomous and community enterprise." If his trustees were not of this opinion, the money should be given to the university. Clearly, Mr. Bell's suspicions remained.

Against this background, Dr. Irving Davidson became Crest's first full-time medical director.

Irving Davidson was forty-three years old when he arrived at Crest. Tall and slim, partially balding, he appeared older than his years, an impression strengthened by his air of mature confidence. Many people regarded Davidson as aggressive in the most positive sense—a leader, a driver, a man with high aspirations, capable of putting them into effect. "Davidson . . . was thought of by many of us to be a kind of messiah; he was of strong character and a decisive man, and he would come and really build Crest into its rightful place."

Arriving in Columbia in March, 1954, Dr. Davidson knew of
the controversy although he was perhaps not fully aware of its
implications. He says:

> When I did come to Crest, a three-way controversy was
> raging; the conflict between the board of trustees and the
> consulting staff; the confusion of relationships between
> the board of directors and the professional staff at Crest;
> and the relationship of the professional staff of Crest and
> the consulting staff to each other. I was given the many
> sides of this conflict; and I was reassured, on all sides, that
> the conflict would resolve itself once we got a full-time
> medical director at Crest, and that all things would be
> subservient to the establishment and development of the
> best kind of psychiatric services for the Crest Foundation.
> It was implied that this was the Foundation that would
> give service to the community, and establish itself as a
> treatment, training, and research center. It was on this
> basis that I accepted the position, even though I knew
> that great conflict between the staff, the board of trustees
> and the consulting staff existed. I think that had an effect
> on the relationship of the development and growth of
> Crest. There was great promise that was held up before
> me, by people interviewing me about Crest and its fu-
> ture, and there was also promise in the things I saw for
> myself as I looked over the Crest Foundation on my visits
> there. After talking with many members of the board and
> consulting staff, and others, I was reassured of the co-
> operation, and was given confirmation and affirmation
> that my ideas were in accord with their own; and I came
> with great enthusiasm.

Among Crest directors, Irving Davidson was particularly well
qualified. A general practitioner before World War II, he entered the service and rose rather rapidly to a position of high
administrative responsibility. After the war Dr. Davidson received psychiatric training from the Menninger staff while serving as a staff member. During his time in Topeka, Dr. Davidson
functioned as chief for varying clinical services, including the

most acutely disturbed ward, as well as the active treatment wards for the more chronic character-disorder patients. He was well-liked by the residents and staff members who worked with him, and was known to be a fine teacher, who particularly enjoyed and stimulated active discussion. He had undergone a didactic analysis; at the time of his arrival at Crest he required only a few more control hours to complete his analytic training.

Thus, Dr. Davidson was a man who had extensive experience in administration, teaching, the treatment of hospitalized mentally ill, and psychoanalysis. In addition, in his last year or so at Topeka, he had been closely involved with a research project, and his interest and involvement with research were also genuine. It is noteworthy that the board, feeling the economic pinch, had decided to offer up to $14,000 to a director on the basis of a minimum of thirty hours a week. Dr. Davidson was not interested in a part-time position at Crest; he wished to devote his full time to the work. The decision to accept $15,000 for a full-time position was his, at his insistence. The salary was low for a person of his experience and background. It appears that he was genuinely interested in the development of Crest, and in total involvement for himself.

The consultants were instrumental in the choice of Dr. Davidson. They were particularly interested in obtaining a man from the Menninger Foundation, someone who shared their philosophy of treatment. Dr. Phelan, who knew Davidson well, strongly endorsed his selection. Davidson was highly recommended by Dr. Karl Menninger. One consultant stated that the professional people who knew Davidson made the choice.

> I don't know who was principally instrumental, but I think, again, Crawford was, and Clark was, and some of the other consultants were. He was from Menningers; they knew him there—and I think, enticed him out here. They felt he could run it according to the principles they established in the first place.

Mr. Bell and the board, of course, had to lean on the professionals in this choice. The strengths and weaknesses of the parties to the power battle were illuminated in this situation: Mr. Bell and the board were forced to rely upon the professional people for professional and clinical decisions, while the professionals were dependent upon Mr. Bell and other laymen for money.

Into this muddy conflict Dr. Davidson entered. The effects of his early actions specifically and directly increased the autonomy of Crest, and of Irving Davidson as the director of Crest. His decisions were subject to serious criticism retrospectively; even then, they raised some question. Davidson was aware of the difficulties of his position in light of the conflict between Mr. Bell and the professionals; he must have realized that no independent move of his could avoid irritating some parties, if not all.

Dr. Davidson took hold of the directorship, and began to forge ahead with the grand-scale opportunities he envisioned for Crest. He expressed this point of view immediately, as can be seen in the newspaper reports of the press conference called upon his arrival.

"The Crest organization has achieved wonders in its three years of operation," Dr. Davidson said. "I am finding the program already underway a very exciting one which offers the staff a continuing challenge to meet its high standards."

Dr. Davidson said plans for the future include expansion of the educational program for training of psychiatrists, psychologists and psychiatric social workers, and eventually to develop a research program.

Closer association with the University Medical School, and additional community services are also expected, Dr. Davidson said.

"In the manner of treatment, we envision a day-hospital program to augment our in-patient department, and we hope to develop a child-psychiatry program to parallel our adult-psychiatry work," Dr. Davidson said.

Under the day-hospital program, patients would remain at the hospital for treatment during the day, but would return to their homes at night, he explained. Group therapy will be starting soon, to add to the occupational therapy, recreational therapy, psychotherapy, psychoanalysis, and other forms of treatment already provided.

Dr. Davidson stated elsewhere: "My expectations were that it would develop into one of the primary training, teaching, and treatment centers of the country, with growth in areas of child psychiatry as well as adult psychiatry."

One of Davidson's early actions affecting the autonomy of the hospital was reported at his first board meeting, in March, 1954. The minutes capsule it: "Mr. Johnson announced his resignation from the position of hospital administrator effective July 1, 1954."

It should be noted that the by-laws of the Crest Foundation at that time read:

> The Board of Trustees shall select and employ a competent experienced administrator, who shall be its direct executive representative in the management of the Foundation. This administrator shall be given the necessary authority and be held responsible for the Administration of the Foundation in all its activities and departments subject only to such policies as may be adopted, and such orders as may be issued by the Board of Trustees or by any of its committees to which it has been delegated power for such action. He shall act as the "duly authorized representative" of said Board in all matters in which the Board has not formally designated some other person for that specific purpose.

Thus, not unlike most general hospital structures, the hospital administrator was designated the principal executive of the foundation. Martin Johnson had been the "director" of the hospital through the period of its first three years and beyond. The temporary, part-time medical directors had concerned themselves almost totally with the clinical aspects of the hospital, but Johnson had in fact run it. He had formally reported to the board, which had held him responsible for the running of the institution, and they considered him very capable. Although the previous part-time medical director had not been regularly invited to board meetings, Mr. Johnson was regularly expected.

Dr. Davidson took a different view of the proper prerogatives of the administrator as balanced against his own. He quickly acted to take over the total leadership of the hospital. The change for Mr. Johnson was too great. He stated:

> I had my feelings hurt terribly when the medical director Davidson came in and it was made very clear that he would be in charge of the hospital and not me. And, of course, shortly thereafter I left. . . . I tried to get the board to make up a chart of organization, and it was indicated that the decisions would be made by Davidson rather than myself, and a marked difference in our salaries, so I left.
>
> Well, you see what it's like. I think I've indicated that I felt the responsibility for the hospital, and the hospital was at least a financial success. At the time when someone else took over the responsibility along with it, the deflating of the ego situation as far as I was concerned, why I lost interest in it also. . . . The part-time directors were smart in their handling of me. I had the feeling that if I weren't the administrator, at least I was co-equal with them. It depends an awful lot on the man you've got out there and you needed an able man to make the hospital function, someone who had drive and would also need to have recognition in terms of prestige. . . . It was not my hospital, but at least it was a part-time situation, you see, and Dean and Jones I knew and worked closely together, and Daniel too. . . . (In other words, they left all the administrative responsibility up to you and they just took the medical responsibility?) That's right. I think that is it because I'm clearly not qualified to take medical responsibility. And they were accessible and I could talk about my problems with them and I learned a lot.

Upon Johnson's resignation, Davidson engaged Henry Jarvis, a psychiatric aide at Crest, as hospital administrator. The board had no part in this decision. Jarvis' background for the job of hospital administrator was almost nonexistent; he had some bookkeeping experience and was considered to be adequately bright. Jarvis as administrator was quite a change from Johnson; clearly, he would in no way threaten Dr. Davidson's leadership. (It is noteworthy that in retrospect a number of board members, particularly the businessmen, felt that the loss of Martin Johnson was crucial in the ultimate failure and demise of Crest.)

Dr. Davidson took still other actions to consolidate his own authority and to increase the autonomy of Crest. It soon became apparent that he was separating himself and the institution from those consultants and other professionals who up to now had been intimately involved with the clinical operation of Crest. For example, Dr. Phelan had, until Davidson's time, been a weekly consultant at Crest staff conferences. Almost immediately, Davidson told Phelan that he was no longer needed as a consultant. Also, Dr. Davidson never consulted with the previous medical director, Dr. Philip Daniel.

Davidson's early moves toward independence roused a good deal of anger in the consultant staff. They also gained him the reputation of siding with Mr. Bell in his suspicions against the Columbia Clinic. Many of the consulting staff, former Menningerites, had known Dr. Davidson and liked him personally. These associates felt that Davidson's dealing with the consulting staff was tactless. They complained of Davidson's grandiosity, citing, as an example, his press interview. (It should be noted that Davidson's statement was not unlike that offered by Dr. Crawford to the Board of Trustees on December 28, 1950, three months after the hospital opened. The minutes note: "Dr. Crawford envisioned the possibility that there might someday be a 'Crest School of Psychiatry,' a 'Crest School for Children,' etc. . . .")

Some of the objections of the consulting staff are explicit in the following sampling:

> Davidson wanted to direct the consulting staff, and wanted to use them in his own way, but was somewhat fearful the consulting staff were going to try to impose their ideas on him; and he didn't want anybody interfering with how he thought he should run the place.

Well, I think as we talk about this a little more, I think that was probably the main reason that things didn't go well, that Irv really tried to set up a little kingdom out there, and that everyone just felt that they were summarily dismissed from whatever they had been doing. And in a very short period of time, I don't know of anyone who developed, toward whom more animosity developed than toward Irv Davidson. And it was a peculiar thing, I never did quite understand it. I never did. Because Jesus, Irv was a pleasant enough guy when you'd talk with him. It just didn't seem to make sense. And Phelan had been responsible largely for getting Irv to come out here.

There was a large dissatisfaction about his flamboyant ways, too, big time in some sense or other that I don't understand. I do remember one hot consulting staff meeting out there where Dean and Davidson were going at it hammer and tongs about Davidson feeling that we wanted to clip his wings and keep him from flying his full glory and this expression "clipping wings" was being tossed around a good deal. He used to antagonize everybody too, at these staff meetings, with wild ideas. And he would say them in such a way I used to say to him afterwards: Irv, you're rubbing everybody's fur the wrong way, you're irritating, antagonizing, take it easy, take it slow, quiet down. Well this was Irv, he was just this way.

A few months after his arrival, Dr. Davidson instituted another innovation which aroused antagonsim—this time, among the powers of the psychoanalytic community, the only outside professional group supporting Crest. In June and July, two senior residents came to Crest, Dr. James Dale and Dr. William Plant, the latter having completed two years of training in Topeka. As part of the residents' training program, Dr. Davidson set up an evening seminar on psychoanalysis. The content of the seminar was to be a discussion of Freud's writings, with Davidson as teacher and leader. Moreover, Davidson did not limit the group to Crest residents and staff. He sent notices of the seminar to the

Veterans Administration and to the university, publicizing it generally.

Psychoanalytic training in Columbia, as in a number of other communities, was the sole property of a closed group: the psychoanalytic center, which was associated with the American Psychoanalytic Association. The senior psychoanalysts in the community, Crawford, Clark, Phelan, and others, guarded this property jealously. Only formal candidates of the Analytic Society received psychoanalytic training. Numerous analytically-oriented, nonmedical people in the community had complained that it was impossible for them to acquire any advanced psychoanalytic training. The analytic group was more or less a closed one.

Dr. Davidson's training had not been yet completed; he was still a candidate. The hierarchical structure within the psychoanalytic group in Columbia—as in many other places—was a strict one. For Irving Davidson to set himself up as a person giving training in psychoanalysis—particularly after he had rebuffed Dr. Phelan and, it seemed to many, aligned with Mr. Bell—could be seen only as a further challenge, a widening of the breach between Crest and the leaders of the analytic group. One of the analysts, very friendly to Dr. Davidson, in commenting on the sources of Davidson's difficulties, noted: "Well, I think the unwarranted expansiveness was one thing. I think that a kind of setting up a little—if you please—psychoanalytic training group aside from the old group was another way." Davidson's group proved quite popular. A number of the younger psychiatrists attended regularly, as did some psychologists.

The professionals were further alienated when Crest, for the first time, began to accept out-patients directly from the community. Dr. Davidson noted:

> I do think there was concern by some that we might be growing too fast and too rapidly, and that there was definite opposition by some that we do not set up any out-patient department, as they felt this might be evidence of competition with the local professional people. However,

an out-patient department did develop, by the very nature of the fact . . . that they were hospital patients
who were discharged and who did return to the hospital
for further continuing contact with their hospital doctor.
We did not have plans for a large out-patient department . . . though there were a few, I think a handful of
people that were accepted as out-patients. I recall . . .
two patients who were admitted directly to the out-patient department, by virtue of the fact that they were
intimately connected with interested people of Crest
Foundation who made contributions. . . . These few
people were accepted directly, but they did not affect the
general policy that there would be no out-patients accepted
in the true sense of an out-patient department. . . .

Meanwhile, Crest was receiving publicity in the newspapers; it
was acquiring a "national reputation." The possibility that Crest
would draw patients away from community psychiatrists,
through its reputation as well as through the acceptance of out-
patients, was talked about a good deal. One of the consultants
noted:

I don't think it was very important personally. I'm trying
to remember—this all came up at one meeting, and there
were certain regulations. I think they were supposed to
be referred by someone on the consulting staff if they
were treated psychotherapeutically, something like that.
But I don't think, at least I wasn't aware of any great
friction, it was more theoretical.

One analyst stated:

Davidson was suspect as someone who was trying to treat
patients himself. I don't know, he behaved to some extent like a guy who was collecting a private practice
while he was there, which I think is human nature; but, I
mean, he wasn't there for that.

It is difficult to evaluate the validity of this complaint. Columbia Clinic, which supplied the majority of the patients from the
immediate area, rarely grew concerned about economic compe-

tition. The time of the Columbia Clinic therapists was well-filled; and they were pleased to have their patients treated by the Crest staff. But while competition as such did not greatly affect the Columbia Clinic, it has been suggested that some of its analysts feared that the publicity accorded Crest might woo away wealthy contacts in the community. Whether or not this fear existed, the consultants later did deal with Crest as if the out-patient issue was important.

But while resentment against Davidson accumulated in the professional community, his relations with the Board of Trustees were highly amicable, apparently until the end of his tenure.

At his first appearance at a board meeting, in March, 1954, Davidson

> solicited the continuing interest of the Board in the work of the hospital and requested direction from the Board as to overall policies. Dr. Davidson stated he had many hopes and plans for future development at the hospital, but that these would of course be subject to the Board's approval and direction.

In telling the board of his plans for the future, Davidson suggested that the development of the board and the membership of the foundation needed to progress hand-in-hand with that of the hospital staff, and that a comprehensive educational program was essential to a top-quality therapeutic program. He hoped to have further collaboration with the school of medicine at the university and to develop a research effort in part independent of, in part a collaboration with the university. Increasing collaboration with other community agencies, such as the courts, social agencies, and schools, was on his future agenda. The board minutes note:

> In the discussion of Dr. Davidson's remarks, it was the consensus of the Board to give approval and support to the program in broad outline. Several members of the Board stated that Dr. Davidson had presented the Board with a challenging vision for the future and a set of goals toward which to work.

At the end of May, Dr. Davidson reported further to the board that:

> He would like to encourage the beginning of long range planning as to future building and other developments at the hospital. He hoped that a building fund could be established, and plans made for more office space, examining room, laboratory, pharmacy, library and other offices for the staff. He reported that the business office is running smoothly and that Mr. Henry Jarvis can take complete charge in another month with Mr. Martin Johnson retained as a consultant on an hourly basis.
>
> Dr. Davidson urged the Board to review its overall philosophy with respect to the Crest Hospital and if necessary to restate its policies. It is his impression that there may be a need for clarification of certain goals and re-definition of responsibilities as regards the active medical staff [consultants], the full time staff at Crest, and the Board. He raised the question as to whether this might call for some revision of the by-laws.

The board decided, following Davidson's lead, to appoint a building committee, authorizing it to take preliminary steps to obtain a master plan and to begin discussions regarding expansion with an architectural firm.

The above quotations from the board minutes typify Davidson's planning, and his pressures on the board. And the board responded—nor were there any complaints at the time from board members about his "grandiosity." The board president of this period recalled:

> We went along with him. He hit a good note there. The first several months he was doing fine, I think from the standpoint of the board. . . . I recall a couple of meetings when Davidson made either case presentations or program discussions in which everybody felt, "Gee, this is good, [he's] got a good grasp of what is involved here, and has enthusiasm."

Throughout the period of Davidson's stay, the board maintained a high level of enthusiasm about the hospital. A board member who was appointed toward the end of Davidson's directorship said that the board was "completely dedicated," and willing to work for the "whole idea" presented by Davidson—although the board was not clear as to what the "idea" was, nor did it "know quite what it was doing." Nevertheless, board members felt that Crest was effective, and were very much caught up in their responsibilities to the hospital.

As a matter of fact, the hospital was a successful concern in a number of concrete ways. It was filled close to capacity most of the time. With a maximum of thirty-three, the patient census for June, 1954, averaged 30.2; for July, 31.9; for August, 30.6; for September, 30.3; for October, 31.1; for December, 31.5. In May, the two residents, Drs. Plant and Dale were appointed. And, under Davidson's leadership, Crest was becoming more actively involved with other community organizations. Senior medical students at the university were rotating through Crest as part of their clinical instruction. As part of its residency training program, Crest offered consultation service to a Columbia children's home. A relationship with the Veterans Administration was being considered. And Davidson was offering didactic work for other professional people in the community.

Thus, the hospital was filled; it was growing; and its influence and importance in the community were increasing. There were, however, financial problems even then, for old buildings needed renovation, and the accounts receivable were large. Nevertheless, the board's support of the hospital was well warranted.

Davidson's good relationship with the board may have been influenced in part by his special relationship with Mr. Bell. Upon his arrival at Crest, Dr. Davidson took over as therapist for the relative of Mr. Bell who was in the hospital. Over the long previous period of treatment, both at Menningers and at Crest, Mr. Bell had been regarded by staff and doctors as the source of all his relative's troubles. He had been cut off from visiting and was viewed as a meddlesome gadfly. Dr. Davidson's attitude differed markedly. He became friendly with Mr. Bell; he arranged for visits between Mr. Bell and his relative—in short, he saw the total problem and Mr. Bell's role in it differently than anyone else. This change in approach seemed to be helpful to the patient. (After Dr. Davidson's resignation as medical director, when he moved from Columbia, Mr. Bell's relative followed Davidson in order to continue under his treatment.) It is not difficult to understand, in the light of these factors, that Mr. Bell's relationship with Dr. Davidson throughout his stay was quite amiable.

At the hospital, the staff were especially enthusiastic about Dr. Davidson's appointment, the more so because they were greatly pleased with the other appointments that had preceded his arrival. The director of nurses speaking of Dr. George Dunn, said, "Everybody was very pleased when George arrived, and George really sold himself with everybody, and everybody really loved him immediately, just like that." Leonard Paulson rapidly had become an integral part of the staff, communicating energy and ardor. These two professionals were delighted with Davidson's appointment. Both had known him in Topeka, and Dunn, at his first board meeting, "expressed the belief that the sanitarium staff under Dr. Davidson will be a most effective team." Paulson had been associated with Davidson on a research project, had been trained on wards where Davidson was service chief, and was a close personal friend. Paulson felt that the choice was perfect for Crest, and mentioned this belief to all members of the hospital staff. Before long, most of the staff were very excited about the hiring of Davidson.

> Everybody looked forward tremendously to Dr. Davidson's coming as being somebody to kind of draw everything together—not as far as getting along, because I think we did that—but organization, and status in the community, and this kind of thing. Everybody had very high hopes that Dr. Davidson would be the leader to take over—the great white father.
>
> . . . I think this was a mark that people had been waiting for. We got our own director, our own medical staff, and the place sort of became independent of the Columbia Clinic. . . . I think people were pretty much

impressed with Dr. Davidson and his background, and I was impressed. . . .

I always did think Dr. Davidson had more plans than he could ever put into effect in two lifetimes. But it sounded to me as if things were going to work out. . . . Ruth was so enthusiastic . . . George was there then, and Paulson . . . and it looked like a good nucleus on which to build something.

The identity of the hospital was little altered by Dr. Davidson's conflict with the consulting staff. By and large, the hospital staff, including the professional staff, were not aware of these difficulties—evidently, if Dr. Davidson was cognizant of acute problems, he kept them to himself. During Davidson's tenure the hospital was a challenging and satisfying place in which to work. Everything was in a process of change and development. The psychologist, Dr. Paulson, referring to the advent of the full-time professional staff, and admitting the general instability in this new structure, says, "It was fun. I was busy, I was doing lots of things, had my hands in everything." One of the residents stated:

At the time I thought we were Chestnut Lodge, Stockbridge, and Topeka all rolled into one and I felt we were on the verge of great treatment. I think the enthusiasm of the staff must have cured a lot of patients, a lot of patients benefitted, and it was an excellent hospital for what we were doing. I believe, then, for the first six or eight months, that we did a good deal of what was pretty good evaluation and short term treatment. . . . I think the treatment was as good as any psychiatric hospital around.

Miss Nichols was pleased about the new director. She felt that she had been charged with too much direct responsibility for patients. She was glad to be relieved of this pressure as her interest had been turning to education for nursing students. She also felt that the morale of the ward staff was extremely high during this time. She said she was happy to have a medical director who would take over medical responsibility.

The residents, Drs. Plant and Dale, came to Crest with the promised expectation that upon completion of their residency requirements they would become permanent staff members. They did not, therefore, have the attitude of transitoriness common to medical residents. Together with Dunn and Paulson, they became a close-knit professional-social unit, part of the Crest family. They were all young—the oldest, thirty-two—enthusiastic and competent. William Plant recalled that he worked very hard, and that "most of the year was a kind of a blur of working and enjoying it, and feeling that we were learning, and making progress, and accomplishing something, and feeling a very close relationship with the rest of the staff." Miss Nichols added:

> It went pretty well, all told, for the nursing department. I didn't have much trouble. I don't remember any trouble, frankly, with Irving [Davidson], just kind of thinking, well we're here and we're a part of it. But he's not too appreciative and neither is he nonappreciative. At that time Dunn was spending lots of time on the ward. We were seeing a lot of Paulson . . . and so it wasn't quite as important to have the medical director be so close. And then Dale and Plant came, and the hospital was full of doctors, compared to what we had had. [The morale was] fairly high—I think quite high—because all the other people were there, and I think people thought that Dr. Davidson as a director ought to make rounds more, and he didn't know much about what was going on; but because there was Dale and Dunn and all these other people, they weren't too concerned; and there were lots of fine things happening to patients then; and everybody was pretty pleased.

Other members of the staff also felt that the situation at the hospital was good.

> [Communication] became excellent right at this time. Dr. Davidson was always around and never too busy. Dr. Dunn likewise—although Dr. Dunn was a little bit more difficult to talk to, little more reserved—and Dr. Dale and

> Dr. Plant came in as residents, and both of them held very fine classes, aide seminars, and things like this. Incidentally, people used to look forward to Dr. Dunn's classes more than anybody's because he could give the most complete detailed and explicit case histories, without using any notes or anything, of any of the doctors who ever were associated with Crest. And I remember hearing many comments about this, people liked it in general. Then we would throw the thing wide open and you could discuss anything, and he talked to any of them, anytime. I don't remember exactly what year it was, but it was probably the best year of the hospital. . . . I'm sure the whole staff felt the need of a permanent medical director and I know we were overjoyed at the thought of having not one, but two doctors come in on the staff permanently, and the possibility of a residents' program being set up—which was—and Dr. Dale and Dr. Plant came in on it . . . and generally I think the feeling was pretty good.

The hospital was going along fine, but there were difficulties. Early in his year as leader, Davidson was severely criticized for his treatment of two patients. It was felt he offered too little control to one manic woman who caused much disturbance within the hospital. More significant, however, was Davidson's public friendship with an alcoholic patient who had been discharged from the hospital and ostensibly was continuing in outpatient treatment with Davidson. Such behavior was taboo, according to Columbia and Crest professional standards, as it had been in strictly psychoanalytic Topeka. However, this was a problem for only a brief time, as Dr. Davidson soon corrected this behavior. Davidson's action which eventually had the most serious consequences was his hiring of his nephew to fill the job of recreational therapy director. One staff member, quite representative of the total staff, stated:

> John Noldorf was in recreation and he was miserable. I mean no one liked him personally, no one thought he

knew what he was doing, and all of these things I think also were true. I mean . . . Dr. Davidson put him in the job, gave his nephew a job, is what it really amounted to. He wasn't qualified. He was too old [in his middle thirties] for that kind of thing. He didn't have any feeling, as far as I could ever tell, about patient treatment. He just wasn't any good in the job.

Not only was John Noldorf unsuited to his job, not only was he Dr. Davidson's nephew, not only was he not liked by anybody on the staff—in addition, it was alleged that he had some relation with communism. At this time McCarthyism was riding high; and the climate was ripe for such innuendos. And Dr. Davidson had a history of activity in liberal causes and organizations; e.g., the Americans for Democratic Action. Moreover, he had already had a brief tussle with the board when certain of its members urged him to discharge an aide alleged to be a Trotskyite. Since the aide was particularly competent, Davidson firmly resisted; furthermore, he did not feel that her political views had anything to do with her job at Crest. (The professional staff totally supported Davidson in this attitude and action.)

The issue of Noldorf appears to have been the one which led finally to a rift between the board and Dr. Davidson. Complaints about Noldorf's alleged communist involvement reportedly were communicated to board members. Then things began to happen. The minutes of the board of March 3, 1955, state:

There ensued a discussion of the overall administrative situation at Crest hospital, particularly with reference to criticisms that have been raised on the part of members of the consulting staff, . . . and to some extent within the staff itself. It was the consensus of the Board that the criticisms raised and the difficulties described merited further study and evaluation, either by an outside consultant or by a committee of the Board itself. As a first step it was suggested that the president appoint a committee to formulate the criticisms in a more concise and factual form, and to present them to a later meeting of the Board. The president, Mr. Blair, then named himself as chairman, with Dr. Waters [an ex officio board member because of his position at the university] and Crawford to serve on the committee.

At a special meeting one week later, March 10, the board resumed the discussion of the "overall administrative situation at Crest Hospital."

It was the unanimous opinion of the committee that its work was of the nature of review of the first year of Dr. Davidson's administration as medical director. The committee was also unanimous in the opinion that Dr. Davidson's administration had been characterized by so many episodes of poor judgment, poor personnel policies, and insensitivity in dealing with the consulting staff, and the Board of Trustees as to raise serious question as to whether he should be retained as medical director.

It was decided to give Davidson a chance to respond to the criticisms and then to report back to the board. The minutes of March 24 report that the committee had met with Dr. Davidson from 8:00 to 9:30 A.M. on Saturday, March 14.

Nothing had occurred in this discussion to change the committee's opinion as presented to the Board on March 10th. Mr. Blair also reported that Dr. Davidson telephoned him on Tuesday, March 17, stating that he was considering submitting his resignation and requesting Mr. Blair's advice. Mr. Blair stated that he advised Dr. Davidson that in his opinion, Dr. Davidson had lost the confidence of a majority of the Board.

A letter of resignation, dated March 17, to take effect July 31, signed by Dr. Davidson was read. It was accepted.

Board minutes omit at least as much as they state; in this case they omit a great deal. To begin with, it seems clear that the "Red" issue was important in the board's consideration. Two board members were very specific:

The first thing we knew he hired a nephew without clearance, which was a mistake, and then we later found out he had a communist record and probably had some sort of a hold on Davidson, so that he was afraid to not appoint him, and that kind of started the beginning of the end. . . . See, Davidson violated all the instructions by hiring a nephew without clearing it, you see. . . . He was just a big shot, kind of a big-shotty individual and tended to alienate people, he just didn't work into the community or any place too well.

And that was one of the unfortunate situations, where numerous derogatory items were dug up about him—anti-American things of that type—so the board had to take action on the things. These things were personal, but since the hospital depended to a large extent on public contributions, anything of that nature would be a detriment to accomplishing the purpose.

Another board member, on the committee that spoke with Davidson, felt that Karl Menninger did not tell all about Davidson, politically, that is, when he recommended him so highly. He added, uncomfortably:

He [Davidson] was caught up. I'm going to be a little vague, because this was a pretty rough go—but he was sort of engulfed, I think in some things not of his own doing and—I mean I have to be a little cute on this; I'm not going to blow off all over the place, because Davidson never hurt me a bit. I always liked the guy, as a matter of fact, and I was a little reluctant to be one of the guys that pulled the chain on him, so to speak. But . . . [we] talked over his area of responsibility, his area of lack of responsibility, and we said: "Look, we think you are a little bit trapped in this thing, and you simply can't deliver under the circumstances, and we are just going to give you the opportunity to resign." And he said: "Is that it?" And we said: "Yeah, that's it." So he said: "Well, I guess that's it then, and, give me thirty days, and I'll dig out," and he left.

Some of the younger consultants also viewed the communist issue as important in effecting Davidson's departure:

> There was always this talk about Red activities and so on, that involved his nephew, I think. That was sort of the tail end of it though. That was kind of a red herring. It was used as a reason.

> I'm still griped to this day that it's rumor, all I have is rumor, and I was very put out and so were others on the consulting staff, that Davidson was actually canned. We were told about it later, and I think this was the beginning of the McCarthy period. We all felt that we were living it in our daily lives, because somehow this guy was quietly given the ax by certain people, without any open discussion or any forum or any clarification of why. It was this story that he had a relative who was F.B.I. bait on the staff, and that Davidson, with his radical political views, was a dangerous guy to have around there.

Certain board members felt helpless and confused about the matter.

> We were conscious on the board, I think . . . that here was a difference of opinion within the board, too, as far as his personal evaluation was concerned. And there were a number of us who, I think, liked the man personally. And when certain facts were brought out on the board which indicated that it was probably best for the institution that he make a change, and maybe best for Dr. Davidson also, I think most of us went along with that. Then it came to our attention that certainly Mr. Bell had a high regard for him and felt badly that he was leaving; and those of us who had a high regard for Mr. Bell thought, well, maybe we don't have the information right—so we were a little confused, I would say that.

Neither helplessness nor confusion existed on the part of the senior members of the professional group. This was a period of their dominance, and their expressions were clear. According to

Dr. Crawford, Davidson's political views got in Crest's way; in addition, he was an inadequate professional person.

> Dr. Davidson got into trouble, in my opinion, because of confusion over his humanitarian objectives and the realities of Crest's financial position. He did not understand or accept the board's position to the effect that Crest had to be a "going concern" before it could expect significant gifts for part-pay or free beds for other philanthropic contributions of its own. He seemed to expect the board somehow to pick up the tab for patients admitted by him who could not pay. He also apparently got the purposes and philosophy of Crest confused with his own personal, social and political views and tended, it seemed, to want to make it a part of some crusade. Whatever the merits of such views, there is no surer way of losing friends and alienating people—patients, relatives, board members, etc.—upon whom a new hospital depends for its survival.

> As you know, it was a board decision to ask for Dr. Davidson's resignation. Although he had been well-recommended, it appeared that he was good as second-in-command, not as the chief. We learned later that some persons, almost as well known, were by no means as favorable to him as Dr. Karl Menninger had been. In any case, my general evaluation of Dr. Davidson was shared by a number of others prior to the time he was asked to leave.

Dr. Davidson's forced resignation was related to the struggle for power, just as his appointment had been. Davidson arrived in the context of an intense conflict between Mr. Bell and the professionals, with Mr. Bell the victor. Davidson's departure left Mr. Bell in a different position. He had not anticipated the professionals' action to remove Dr. Davidson, and could not prevent it. Here Bell was helpless, dependent on the professional group. Another board member also felt this dependency:

> This permeated to the board; and the reason that the board finally agreed to have him go, or insisted that he

did leave, to the best of my recollection, was the accusation which came to us that he was not a man of integrity, that you could not believe what he was saying. Well, this was a pretty basic criticism of a man, and I will confess that in my limited relationships with him I had completely no evidence of this, and no way to judge the man; and we had to rely on the staff's recommendation as to his ability as a medical director; and they insisted that he was failing in this. We wondered on the board . . . at the conflicting information that we got from various members of the consulting staff, and this confused us; and we probably made decisions that were very unwise, possibly in regard to Davidson.

That the power struggle was the most prominent factor operative in the discharge of Davidson is further indicated by the fact that the professionals, aside from the senior people—although they had been critical of him—were ambivalent about seeing him leave. The man who was then president of the consulting staff said:

The board finally asked the consulting staff if they would fire Davidson. And I happened to be president of the consulting staff at that time. I'll never forget, Crow and Waller and I met over at Waller's house, and I told them, as an executive committee, I told them what we had been asked to do. And we just kind of laughed about this: why the hell should the consulting staff, who was never paid any attention to anyway, be given the job of doing some distasteful thing, you know. And we said we absolutely wouldn't do it, this was a function of the board.

The hospital staff was shocked and puzzled. The announcement of the director's leaving came with no prelude, no warning. Although some difficulties had occurred, and there was unhappiness about Mr. Noldorf, everything had seemed to be going smoothly at the time Davidson announced his departure. Miss Nichols said:

I think people were real concerned that Irving Davidson had left and nobody quite understood why. I don't think the nursing staff ever really understood why he was fired. Everybody knew he was fired, this was so, and I don't think I really understood it at the time, you know, completely. I knew that it had mainly to do with the Columbia Clinic and the doctors and their dislike of him. . . . I think I knew that this was why he was fired, from their standpoint; but this was not common knowledge with the staff. I don't think they ever really understood this. . . . I felt I had information that I could not be giving staff about this. . . . I don't think anybody knew about the clinic business; and I didn't really know about this, until the very last.

She considered that Dr. Davidson's leaving had a bad effect on the hospital:

I think it was pretty bad, as I recall. I think I'm being very subjective in saying this, though; pretty bad as far as I'm concerned. But somehow this meant that the one and only full-time director that we had had, couldn't make it, and my mind kept running about that. "This isn't just this guy, there are other elements in this."

Another nurse said:

The thing that stands out in my mind is the morning that he announced that he was leaving, and my feeling that he couldn't beat the system.

In spite of the blow of Davidson's departure, the momentum of the growth, identity, and ideology of the hospital was maintained. Even on the board, hopes remained high. The president stated that the board "took it in stride . . . [the high enthusiasm] wasn't affected." And at the hospital the young professional staff was working with undiminished excitement and dedication. One of the staff commented:

I felt badly when he left, and concerned. But we were all excited about the future and felt something good would happen and—it is hard to remember exactly, you know. Those were turbulent days.

CHAPTER FIVE

The Board of Trustees

On May 26, 1955, Dr. Thomas Crawford was elected president of the Board of Trustees. One of his first moves at this meeting was to report that there was considerable unrest among the Crest staff and consulting staff because Dr. Davidson continued to function as a lame-duck medical director. After some discussion the board voted to appoint Dr. George Dunn as acting medical director, effective immediately. Dr. Crawford wrote to him:

> I think it is quite possible, although this is my own personal opinion, that if things go well under your administration and if you continue to command the loyalty and respect of the hospital staff and the consulting staff, many of whom urged your appointment, you will in all probability be made permanent director a year from now if you are still interested.

In fact, very little if any effort was made to find a permanent medical director during the period of Dunn's acting directorship.

A number of persuasive factors favored Dunn's appointment: Davidson was leaving; there was not time to search for a permanent director; and Dunn was immediately available. Moreover,

he wanted the position and campaigned to get it. A few days
before he was appointed acting director, he wrote to the chairman of the board's professional committee:

> Since Dr. Davidson submitted his resignation I have
> given the possibility of my applying for the position of
> Director serious thought and have evolved a number of
> concrete ideas concerning Crest. These include my own
> conception of the philosophy of the Crest Foundation
> and my personal feelings as to how I might most effec-
> tively make this philosophy a working one. Should the
> Professional Committee or the Board be interested in my
> thinking about this, I would welcome the opportunity to
> express these ideas. . . .

Dunn had the support of the hospital staff; he was respected
and well liked by his colleagues, and they communicated their
feelings to the board members, as well as to the local psychiatric
community. Since the board had been told that Davidson's administration was inept, Dunn appeared a welcome solution to
the problem of morale.

Dunn's intelligence and ability were apparent. He has been
described as brilliant, idealistic, extremely articulate, a salesman,
a politician. He was a man of parts, knowledgeable about literature, painting, and music, and was an accomplished pianist and
poet. Discriminating about food and wines, always impeccably
dressed, he was a highly sophisticated person. He was also regarded by his friends as a warm, sensitive human being.

Dunn's appointment was favored not only by his abilities and
his personal charm, but also by the at least tacit support of Dr.
Crawford. Some felt that Crawford "sponsored" Dunn for the
position. At any rate, he did not oppose him.

> I think it was really Tom Crawford who influenced peo-
> ple to accept George. He believed in him. . . . I think that
> Tom's endorsement of George was what swayed the
> Board, because obviously—I mean, Tom is a man who com-
> mands a great deal of respect and liking and affection . . .
> quite a guy.

Dr. Crawford's position with regard to Dunn, however, was viewed critically by some members of the psychiatric community, for Dr. Dunn was at this time an analytic candidate and a patient of Crawford's. Presumably, if his analysis and training went well, he would be eligible for admission as a member of the psychoanalytic association. That Dr. Crawford continued as Dunn's analyst and as board president after the latter's appointment to the medical directorship was considered by some to be irregular and unwise. Dr. Crawford made attempts to alleviate the strain of these circumstances. He reduced his role at the board meetings to one of simply presiding with minimal participation, and set up administrative committees within the board to deal with the issues coming before it. In this way, Dunn would deal directly with the committees, and only indirectly with the board, of which his analyst was president. In spite of these measures, however, a number of those concerned—lay people as well as professional—experienced uneasiness.

> It seemed to me that this was a complicated situation, that the analyst and the medical director . . . I mean, that the medical director and his analyst were there together, directing the board, keeping the board in line, or selling the board on doing something . . . just didn't strike me right.

Dunn's position as medical director was vulnerable on other scores. First, the board was aware that he was relatively young—in his late twenties—for so responsible a position. Second, for the local psychoanalysts, his professional status was low. He was in a didactic analysis, still a candidate for the position of psychoanalyst, and thus dependent upon the local psychoanalytic group for professional advancement. Also, unlike Davidson, he was not an established professional with a prior history of holding responsible positions. He had graduated from an excellent medical school, with honors, had served as a psychiatrist in the armed forces, and had been a fellow at the Menninger Clinic for three years. Thus, he was in a subordinate position vis-à-vis the local psychiatric community. This does not imply that Dunn considered himself subordinate; rather, that in the eyes of important people in the community, he did not have an independent status.

Dunn passed his trial period successfully. He, Ruth Nichols, and Henry Jarvis, the hospital administrator, were formed by the Board of Trustees into an executive committee to run the hospital. All reports indicated that Dunn and this committee administered the hospital very well, and morale was high. He suggested to the board that an additional staff psychiatrist be hired, and he was authorized to do so. He reported that he had tightened the check-up on the finances of prospective patients to make sure they could pay. He proposed that the existing hospital structure be remodeled to make room for more office space, even at the loss of three beds; and this was accepted. He began to revise the inservice training program. A request for a research grant was submitted to the National Institute of Mental Health. He began to discuss with the board the issue of specifying the goals of Crest in the Columbia community.

Dunn himself was aware of the effectiveness of his work. He reported to the board in October that the hospital was running well, and, on October 30, he wrote a letter to Crawford saying that in his opinion he had done well enough to be considered for the permanent medical directorship. On November 24, he reported that a significant number of patients were improving. It is not surprising that on February 23, 1956, he was made the permanent medical director.

Dunn began early to strengthen his position as medical director. One of his first moves was to eliminate the ambiguity of his relationship to the hospital administrator. He suggested a new by-law to change the system from one in which the hospital administrator had an equal status with the medical director vis-à-vis the board, to a system under which the hospital administrator would report directly to the medical director, Dunn. The board adopted his suggestion. This change was in line with the subordination of the administrator to the medical director, the system Davidson instituted. The change in the by-laws also made more explicit Dunn's power to hire his own administrator and other personnel. At this time the discovery of an embezzlement by the hospital administrator—although Dunn had planned to change in advance of it—argued for its acceptability.

The embezzlement was discovered accidentally; Dr. Plant was making a routine check of an ex-patient's complaint of being erroneously charged, and found a receipt which was obviously forged. This required further investigation. A board member, who was an accountant, Martin Johnson, the former administrator, and Dr. Dunn spent hours over the books. They discovered that Jarvis had been taking small amounts of money steadily; the sum totaled approximately $8,000. Jarvis was bonded and so the hospital took no loss. Surprisingly, knowledge of the embezzlement was limited, at the hospital, to the professional staff. Martin Johnson offered to carry the administrator's load temporarily. Some months later John Hanson, a sober, capable bookkeeper-accountant was hired.

As director, Dunn was very different from his predecessor. He did not personally supervise the functioning of the hospital, as Davidson had done. Instead, he delegated much authority in the care of patients to his professional colleagues.

Although his communication with the ward staff was not close and tended to be erratic, the ward staff had a close relationship with other professional personnel, particularly with Dr. Dale, who conducted classes in the theory of milieu treatment and made great efforts to maintain communication with all the staff. Dale constantly was available for guidance, questions, and discussions, often would visit the hospital in the evening to meet with the night shift, and was considered to be particularly effective in supporting the ward personnel. Dunn was thoroughly informed about the patients and his staff; he had close informal contacts with the professional personnel—Nichols, Plant, Paulson, and Dale—which included a biweekly after-hours literary group.

The staff at the hospital maintained their earlier *esprit de corps* and their unquestioning acceptance of the effectiveness of the hospital. The ward staff maintained a tight social structure, meeting after work at a tavern to talk about Crest, about patients, about common problems. Dunn's goals for the hospital were high, in keeping with the initial ideal of Crest, and seemed to be nearing realization. The ward staff, as did the professional staff, felt that Crest was well along the road to greatness.

Dunn continued to concern himself considerably with his relationship with the board. For example, he attempted to clarify what sorts of matters should be brought up to the board in his reports. He sent letters to all members of the board, asking them which of the following they would be most interested in: "(1) Details of the hospital, of activities; (2) Patient population and treatment program; (3) Overall cost of the hospital; (4) Community functions of the hospital staff." Some of the replies he received illustrate the board's vagueness about its role. A lawyer, a long-time board member, wrote:

> I do not have sufficient experience in work of this character to have any fixed ideas on your problems and am inclined to follow your leadership rather than try to give you any helpful criticism or suggestion. Perhaps later on you may educate me to having ideas of my own. I do enjoy the association with you.

From Dr. Crawford, still president of the board:

> Your question about the nature of your reports finds me without any ready answers. One of the prime questions of course is what is to be the relationship between the Board and the full-time staff at the hospital. And as you know it is my impression that as long as the Board is small, informal and having frequent meetings, your reports may be fairly full, chatty and detailed. As the Board becomes larger, and its meetings infrequent, then your reports of necessity would be more formal and more abstract. Another variable, it seems to me, is the activities of the Board's committees. If the various committees of the Board are fairly active and in close touch with the situation of the hospital, then a good deal will come through the committees. If these relationships again become more formal and more remote then the burden of reporting will fall on you. I can imagine that the time may come when the medical director's report is an annual one given

in the form of a speech at the annual meeting or perhaps even published as a brochure. For the time being, however, I think there is still need for a good deal of "Board education" and that therefore the informal type of report with a fair amount of direct information as to what is going on both within the hospital and in terms of its community activities is what the Board needs. This is all pretty general. I hope it may be helpful.

From a physician:

It seems to me that the Board is interested in the general picture of the hospital and the general policies. It is also always interested in the inpatient census. I would feel that the detailed reports of patient treatment might be minimized unless there is some particularly interesting incident which would illustrate some point.

Of the more intimate matters concerning the hospital staff, morale and relations between hospital staff and the consulting staff are important. Though slightly less intimate but of great interest would be plans and progress of educational and research programs. Of the more externalized, the Board would be interested in relations between the hospital staff and the medical profession generally, contacts with the medical profession within the hospital, and publicity and public relations in general.

This no doubt parallels your own thoughts and, of course, it would not be necessary to cover all these points at each meeting, and it certainly does not preclude mention by you of anything which you feel would be of interest and of value for the information of the Board.

The tone and generality of these replies make it plain that the board members thought it was up to Dunn to decide what they should hear. The great dependence of this voluntary board, largely made up of lay people, on the professional directorship, is evident. Actually, Dunn's reports about the functioning of the hospital had been rather impressive to the board. The members saw him as extremely articulate; sometimes, indeed, his descriptions of the functioning of the hospital were even eloquent. He often presented case material in disguised form and this pleased the board.

Dunn's reports to the board during the first two years of his administration were positive; the hospital was healthy as a business and was doing effective clinical work. His judgment about the functioning of the hospital was backed up by the only two types of factual, "objective" data that could be offered to the board to evaluate the hospital: first the census; second, the balance sheet. These two were understandable to the businessmen on the board, and became extremely important to the board members. At each meeting they expressed great interest in whether the patient census had been above the break-even point during the previous month. Some members later described the board's interest in the census and balance sheet as being almost obsessional.

Nevertheless, with this data, Dunn was able to demonstrate that the hospital was doing well. He had early stabilized the financial situation which had been shaky under Davidson. Patients no longer were admitted without an investigation of their ability to pay. Further, the financial situation during this period was stabilized by the larger revenues coming to the hospital from psychotherapy. Psychotherapy fees were always additional to the basic hospital charge, and many patients continued in psychotherapy after leaving the hospital. In psychotherapy fees alone, almost all the professional people earned for the hospital considerably more than enough to pay their salaries.

The census was no longer a problem, Dunn reported to the board in October, 1956. There was a waiting list, and referrals were coming in steadily. To the board members then there was strong cause to feel enthusiastic about the hospital and about their leader George Dunn. An officer of the board stated:

> I think the atmosphere of the group—of the board—was that the staff at Crest were doing a good job: the therapy was well administered; the patients were given tremendously fine and persistent care; and that their record of accomplishment and improvement of the patients was as

good or better than any of the other hospitals, reflecting
back on the need for these very high standards. Now I
can't say that was the result of statistics, but it was regularly referred to when the question of census came up;
and the patients would be referred from these distant
places because of the good job that was being done, the
confidence that these doctors had.

In retrospect, some of the board members report that they
were somewhat suspicious of Dunn. Their complaints, unquestionably colored by hindsight, were based particularly on the
character of his reports.

George always painted such a glowing picture of everything, and waxed so poetic about Crest every time he had
the chance to talk about it at board meetings, which was
frequent. And I . . . can't claim any special clairvoy-
ance, but I thought here was a very unusual person that's
beyond my particular scope of experience. And I
couldn't make up my mind whether he was very bright,
very able and unusual, or whether there was a big façade
here, that maybe didn't have much behind it.

If such doubts did exist at the time they certainly did not
become serious. Those board members who retrospectively reported some skepticism also noted that they did not feel free to
discuss their doubts with other board members, an indication
they did not feel that their doubt was shared. On the whole the
board members *believed* in Dunn and Crest, because they had
concrete evidence on which to base their belief and a strong need
to believe.

The consultants, however, were more critical. One stated:

These were the first board meetings I ever attended officially, and I was embarrassed and uneasy and a little
angry. . . . Dunn was called upon in the meeting to say
things. I felt he was distinctly coloring his reports in a
grandiose way, and leading the board down the trail of
something or other that was just unrealistic, in his talking about Crest's great fame and scientific importance in

the field of psychiatry and psychology. He just talked in a grandiose way, as though he were buttering up the board, as though he were selling the board something, selling the board their hospital. . . .

It was terrible because it was not factual. I don't think, I know Dunn's reports were not factual, just not. And that what he did was as if to continually, with the Board of Trustees, build up this idea that this was going to be a tremendous research and teaching institution, and that he just far oversold the place. . . . The whole thing just became too unrealistic from every viewpoint, and actually the treatment began to get neglected in favor of— well, not sales talk—but a whole bunch of hot air, some of which was true. . . .

The criticism was a minor strain. Things were going well with the hospital and Dunn's leadership was supported by both the board and the hospital staff. In this context he presented dramatic plans for the long-range growth of the hospital. He had begun to develop his plans even before he became the permanent medical director. In August, 1955, he wrote a long letter to the board presenting a choice of two possible goals for Crest:

A choice is now posed which is rather explicit. This choice necessitates essentially a statement of treatment policy. Subsumed by this choice will be the education and research functions of the Crest Foundation. With our present facilities and tentative plans for the coming year, there appear to be two choices: [one,] the Crest Foundation Hospital should be considered a sanitarium providing an analytically oriented milieu for patients referred by members of the consulting staff, which staff members in great part will meet the psychotherapeutic demands of the patients referred to the hospital.

If this is to be the direction of Crest's growth, educational opportunities will be available for one or at the most two third-year psychiatric residents whose experience and supervision will probably come from the consulting staff. Research would most probably have to be done on an individual basis. A permanent medical staff of two, director and assistant, with the assistance of residents, could meet the managering demands of hospital patients. The staff could also provide some inservice training. They could not assume more than a few psychotherapeutic responsibilites.

[Two,] the Crest Foundation should be a self-contained psychiatric unit to which patients can be referred for intensive psychoanalytically oriented treatment in a hospital setting, wherein the psychotherapeutic needs of these patients, with few exceptions, can be met by members of the hospital staff.

If this is the direction chosen, we have to concentrate on the securing of qualified permanent staff who can assume the gamut of psychotherapeutic activity. At the present time, Crest would require at least one qualified analyst interested in psychotherapy of psychotic patients and severe character disorders. There should be at least two full-time members on the medical staff who can assume relatively unsupervised psychotherapeutic responsibilities.

The medical director should be able to spend at least 20 hours each week in educational, administrative and supervisory activities.

Dunn was really not offering a choice. The only direction for this growing, progressive, successful hospital was the second type; Crest would be an autonomous hospital, actively treating its own patients. Dr. Dunn had the same general plans for the hospital as had Dr. Davidson.

The problems and goals presented by Dunn's letter were discussed at several subsequent meetings of the board, but no formal action was taken. However, Dunn's thinking on these matters continued to develop and his plans took more definite shape. In February, 1956, he wrote to Mr. Joseph Bond, the new president of the Board of Trustees, that the existent facilities at the hospital were inadequate and that new ward buildings were needed. Finally, in January, 1957, he presented a thorough plan for a general expansion of Crest into a comprehensive, independent hospital.

Dunn's plans focused on Crest's concentration on long-term cases requiring extended psychotherapy. The hospital staff were to be responsible for the psychotherapy in these cases. This goal was supported by the board, although not explicitly, and, interestingly enough, by the local psychiatric community. The chairman of the consulting staff as early as 1955 had indicated their support of this view of the hospital's goals.

In fact, Crest had already taken this direction, as was indicated by the change in the average length of stay in the hospital shown in the following figures:

Year	Average Length of Stay—Days
1951	48.1
1952	43.8
1953	51.5
1954	28.4
1955	100.9
1956	82.7
1957	86.6

In 1955 there was a sharp rise in the average length of stay from the previous years. This increased length of stay was maintained in 1956 and 1957, the major period of Dunn's administration.

The percentage of patients receiving physical treatment dropped markedly after 1955, and the number receiving psychotherapy increased greatly. In fact, almost all the patients in the hospital from that time on were in psychotherapy. During this time and later the idea of "psychological treatment for the psychologically ill" dominated Crest. Psychotherapy and milieu therapy became the treatments of choice and of emphasis.

In Dunn's comprehensive plan he spoke of a possible specialization in problems of adolescents, particularly schizophrenics. Few hospitals in the country were equipped to deal with these problems on any large scale, and few were interested in these difficult patients. During the first two years of his directorship, Dunn periodically reported that a high percentage of new admissions were adolescents. In his long-range plan he envisioned such a concentration as a unique function of Crest. The hospital staff supported his choice; it was another aspect of the uniqueness of Crest and a step in Crest's growth. The Board of Trustees supported wholeheartedly the plan for specialization in adolescents.

Dunn's comprehensive plan also included the expansion of research programs, the educational function of the hospital, and the day hospital program. All of these projects were effected; for example, a research design was developed and a grant proposal was submitted to the National Institute of Mental Health. Dunn's plans also required considerable expansion of the physical facilities of the hospital. He wrote:

> In analyzing the developmental plan for Crest it becomes obvious that any further expansion must be coordinated with an expansion of the physical plant. Thus major emphasis must immediately be placed upon beginning construction of an entirely new hospital. It is more appropriate to plan a unit by unit development. This unit by unit development must be within the framework of a well considered total hospital plan.
>
> I suggest we contemplate construction initially of a twenty-five bed hospital unit which will be partially restricted. . . . With this increase in the number of patient facilities it becomes mandatory to consider a simultaneous construction of a recreational therapy building and new dining and kitchen facilities. The dining and kitchen facilities should be planned so as to be adequate for the needs of the total eventual hospital. Although I suggest plans for the immediate construction of a twenty-five bed unit it is essential that the first step in this program be the planning of an entirely new hospital of which this suggested unit will be but a part. This will involve architectural planning, careful consideration of the needs of the total hospital, etc.

These plans were similar to those proposed by Davidson during his directorship.

Part of the purpose of expansion was to provide facilities for specialized units in geriatrics, children, and adolescents. The hospital, in short, was to be a complete psychiatric facility, with emphasis on long-term psychotherapy for a wide variety of patients. It was to be considerably larger. In February, 1956, Dunn recommended to the board that it plan for a patients' building which would also provide additional office space. In July, 1956, a committee of the board, including a local architect and Dunn, went to work on plans for a fifty-bed hospital. However, the committee gave highest priority to the construction of a hospital office wing and redecoration of patients' rooms. Concentration on office space was quite disappointing to the hospital staff, which had expected Dunn to propose an expansion of the activities building. The need for an activities building was especially acute if the emphasis on the treatment of adolescents was to continue.

The plans for the physical expansion of the hospital required some activity from the board; up to this point all they had been expected to do was to go along with Dr. Dunn. But for the implementation of the physical plan, the raising of capital funds was inescapable. Although some board members viewed Dunn's plans as rather grandiose, in general the board reacted favorably. They set about trying to find ways of raising money.

In August, 1956, the board discussed the possibility of raising funds for a down payment on the expanded facilities of the hospital. They decided to investigate the problem with a local banker, an absentee board member. At the September meeting, it was reported that the banker advised approaching institutions which specialized in hospital financing. The board also discussed expanding membership to "more men and women who are widely known in the community who might command the interest and support of others in a position to make substantial donations to the hospital." One of the annual membership drives was being conducted at this time, and Hanson, the administrator, reported that $1,343 had been raised. The possibility of hiring a professional fund raiser was discussed. Philanthropic foundations were yet another possible source of funds; Dunn said at this meeting that he would draft a letter to such foundations.

These efforts, however, did not bear fruit. By November, 1956, the board learned that the foundations would support research, training, and education, but not capital expansion. In March, 1957, they found that the banks had rejected the possibility of a loan stating their opinion that the expansion of the hospital was strictly a local problem. After these two rebuffs, no further attempts were made to secure funds for the expansion of the hospital. Nor were efforts to gain community support much more successful. The board members had great difficulty in approaching the community for support, in part because Crest's services to the community never were clarified completely, and because Crest appeared to be a hospital for the wealthy, since its fees rose steadily over the years.

One sizeable donation, however, did come in. The Ford Foundation contributed $15,000 to Crest as part of a program of making grants to all nonprofit hospitals in the country. This money was used to begin the planned patient and office building. It was never completed, and the carefully designed, unused and unusable structure was still sitting ghostlike in a prominent place on the Crest grounds at the time of the close of the hospital.

It was about this time, after he had occupied the position of medical director for approximately two years, that Dr. Dunn's behavior began to change. At the hospital he had become negligent about attending staff meetings and about arriving at work on time. He had used poor clinical judgment in some cases, establishing excessively close relationships with some of the patients. But there were more serious signs of deterioration in his behavior. He had made an impulsive marriage—indeed, many of his intimate friends regarded it as pathological. He had also been experimenting with drugs, and his physical condition was poor.

At the hospital, Dunn's unfortunate change did not have as disastrous an effect as might be supposed because the hospital leadership was taken over by a group of its professional people. This group—physicians and other professionals at the hospital—had begun to meet regularly with Dunn toward the middle of his administration to coordinate hospital activities and functions. As

Dunn's problems became manifest, his attendance at these meetings grew sporadic. Yet the group continued to meet, to coordinate activities, to establish communication, and so on, among the various departments of the hospital—in short, they assumed the leadership function at the hospital as Dunn began to abdicate it. In this way, they were able to protect the ward personnel from full knowledge of Dunn's deterioration; Miss Nichols reports that she made continual excuses for Dunn's absences. The protective activities of this group of second-level professional personnel were facilitated by the fact that Dunn never had closely supervised or directed the day-to-day administrative functioning of the wards. Thus, the ward staff were able to function with a minimum loss of effectiveness, in spite of the poor performance of the medical director.

It is worth noting here that Dr. Dunn was not the only individual among the professional group who was having personal difficulties; although his, unquestionably, were most significant for Crest. Speaking of this period, one of the professional staff recalled:

> Nearly everybody on the staff was in analysis and everybody's wife was in analysis and everybody's analyst and everybody's wife's analyst was involved. So you had what you might say trouble to the power of four and this compounded the confusion terrifically. It was really compounded because everybody was involved. I imagine that if we had been left alone—were in a big city where the analysts mind their own business and your wife's analyst minds his own business and we just went out to work thirty miles away from the center of the city, it conceivably could have been a little different. But it was a mess. Everybody was in the soup. Everybody had a say-so, everybody had their opinion. I may be projecting, but I think it got into everybody's analysis. Everybody got into analysis and then there was a lot of realization of the pathological aspects of our involvement with the hospital and with each other, some of which I am sure was iatrogenic and some of which I think is valid. I think a lot of

it reflects some of the opinions of various analysts involved; I think some of it reflected the truth.

It is true that the functioning of the hospital began to deteriorate at this time, although not seriously. Communication between most of the residents and the ward staff continued to be good, but there were one or two who now found it difficult to operate effectively. And although classes for the ward staff continued, Dr. Dale and Miss Nichols began to lose interest in them, sometimes not attending. The ward staff was still a well-integrated group, but a split began to appear between the old-timers and the newcomers, who were not so involved in Crest. All still viewed the hospital as therapeutically effective but a gradual decline was sensed.

This slow decline cannot be attributed solely to Dunn's failure as a leader. It also appeared to be a result of the slowing down of the growth rate of the hospital. This is not to say that the hospital did not continue to expand; there were some real strides forward. The hospital received a grant from the National Institute of Mental Health for research concerned with evaluating changes in hospitalized patients. Morris Pattman, a senior analyst, a psychologist, and a leader in psychotherapy at the Menninger Foundation, joined the staff. Yet, neither of these advances was so dramatic and so impressive as the growth of the hospital during its first few years.

The difficulty at the hospital was not public knowledge and it is doubtful that even the board was aware of what was happening. However, a crucial occurrence, resulting in the collapse of the board's image of Dunn's qualities as a medical director, took place at this time. The collapse was an immediate result of an attack on Dunn as hospital administrator and as a person by Dr. Clark. Dr. Clark made his denunciation at a meeting of the board, and in telephone calls to members of the board. He said that Dunn was very sick, mentally; that Dr. Crawford's psychoanalytic treatment of him had been poor; that he was expressing his pathology in his behavior toward patients at the hospital; that he was incapable of properly administering the hospital. He accused Dunn of a serious characterological malady, indicating that his public behavior had reflected poorly on himself and on the hospital. And Clark added that he was no longer sending patients to Crest.

Clark could not have been directly aware of the degree of effectiveness of the hospital. He had primarily to base his judgments on Dunn's behavior. Much later he admitted that he had generalized too much from Dunn to the hospital, and had neglected to consider sufficiently the high caliber of the other professionals working there.

Although Dr. Clark's charges against Dunn possessed validity, the fury with which he made his attack appeared to have other sources. To some degree, his behavior was an outgrowth of his impetuous, passionate temperament. But his depth of feeling about Dr. Dunn appeared to be related to his bitterness toward Dr. Crawford, who had supported Dunn as medical director, and whose patient Dunn had been.

In 1954, three years earlier, Clark and Crawford, partners in the Columbia Clinic, co-founders of Crest, had had a serious personal falling-out. Dr. Crawford had left the Columbia Clinic and the differences that existed between himself and Dr. Clark had not been resolved. They had become leaders of separate factions in the local psychoanalytic community. Their rift—which had nothing to do with Crest—was felt keenly by the institution that they had created.

Their widely differing temperaments and personalities had influenced them in taking different stands on issues of significance to the development of Crest Hospital, as can be seen, for example, in their reactions to Mr. Bell's financial maneuvering. In reference to Mr. Bell's refusal to transform his loan into a gift, Dr. Crawford later said:

> This meant an excessive concentration of power in Mr. Bell's hands and it stood to influence the interest of other potential donors. It was at this point that Dr. Clark and I disagreed. My position was that we could go ahead anyway, that it was unlikely that the "gift" would be withdrawn, that Mr. Conley was in a position to moderate Mr. Bell's wielding of power, and that, in any case, Mr.

Bell was very old and that the situation, at worst, would exist for a relatively short time. Dr. Clark, on the contrary, was increasingly angry and upset by this state of affairs. By his own admission he was so upset about it that he feared that it would affect his health, and it was for this reason that he resigned from the board. [Dr. Clark resigned from the Board of Trustees in January 1954.] Meanwhile, however, this same situation bothered Mr. Blair and other members of the board, but Mr. Conley (as Mr. Bell's attorney) gave repeated unofficial assurances that the gift would not be withdrawn. . . .

This is what Dr. Clark said later:

The mistake was that we did not clarify with the large donors, and work through with them, the fact that this was not a money-making scheme of the Columbia Clinic; and we were accused of this and we acted as though it was so, and this allowed an argument to go on, on the part of Mr. Bell especially. It was destructive for a long [time] . . . I got so tired of this that I talked to others and put forth as strong an argument as I could in favor of getting all this money paid in, or else. Either stop the operation and get the money all in, and stop this stuff. . . . Bell again talked against this, and so I resigned; and it was at this point that Tom Crawford said that I was committing suicide by resigning from the board.

Dr. Clark added, "And he [Dr. Crawford] would not go along and press this . . . 'oh, you mustn't get people upset,' and so on, and so on, and I don't understand this kind of language, so I resigned."

Dr. Crawford stated that there was *no* conflict between Bell and the Columbia Clinic, but rather, that the conflict was between Mr. Bell and Dr. Clark. Another psychiatrist said, "Bell hated Clark so much—Bell was sure that Clark was out to get Bell's money in one form or another." In a similar vein, a board member stated, "Bell was terribly suspicious of Clark—Clark was a Svengali that was going to try to get this hospital for his own, you see, by reaching out from the Columbia Clinic, was going to get hold of this beautiful dough that Bell was giving to Crest."

The conflict between Mr. Bell and Dr. Clark ended by dividing Crawford-Clark—who, at the beginning, had spoken "with the voice of one man." Dr. Crawford was not sympathetic with Dr. Clark's clashes with Mr. Bell. As noted, he did not consider the issue of Bell's withholding the money of great importance. He himself got along perfectly with Mr. Bell. "Bell and others had real confidence in Tom Crawford," says a close observer. Dr. Crawford says, "It would appear . . . that Mr. Bell responded differently to Dr. Clark and me because we responded differently to him!" Of conflicts between the board and the Columbia Clinic—so excruciating to Dr. Clark—Dr. Crawford says, "I do not recall any such conflicts."

The rift between Crawford and Clark also had divided the psychoanalytic community. Dr. Crawford was sensible of the disapproval of him for remaining board president after his patient had become director. His awareness of this criticism was in part responsible for his withdrawal from the board, as is apparent in the letter of resignation he wrote in November, 1956.

> About six months ago or more, I wrote to Mr. Blair indicating my wish to resign from the Crest Board as of the next annual meeting, April 1957. Because of the provisions of the By-laws, I would have to retire from the Board in any case a year from that time, but I think I should get out now because of the fact that analytic patients of mine or relatives of patients are becoming increasingly involved in the work of the Board. As long as contacts with patients are infrequent and casual, they do not interfere significantly with the course of analysis. When such contacts involve decisions affecting those individuals—such as increases in salary and the like—then they may make for considerable interference in the analysis. In any event, I think it is the better part of wisdom for me to retire next spring for the reasons I have mentioned. . . .

After he resigned from the board Dr. Clark at first attempted to cooperate with the new director. When, early in his term, Dunn requested that local analysts conduct seminars at the hospital for staff education, Dr. Clark accepted the invitation. He conducted a didactic control on a patient of Dunn's. That is, Dunn periodically presented reports on his patient at a seminar, where Clark and other members of the seminar contributed suggestions about the treatment of the patient. This experiment did not work out smoothly. Dunn often responded to Clark's suggestions by treating the patient in the opposite way. His rejection of Clark's advice became so chronic that Clark shifted the seminar to the patient of another psychiatrist.

At the time of Clark's denunciation of Dunn to the board, he was not the only doctor who felt that Dunn had become incompetent as a medical director. From a variety of sources—what they heard on the couch, what they heard from Dr. Clark, what they observed of Dunn's description of his work at the meetings of the consulting staff—a number of the local psychiatrists had begun to doubt Dunn and Crest. Some of them had begun to question the value of milieu therapy; some considered that the staff had been too lax in placing limits on patients, especially the adolescent patients; some felt simply that the staff was inexperienced. How much of this feeling was a result of direct knowledge of the operation of the hospital, how much of it was rumor, and how much of it was overgeneralizing from impressions of Dunn, are intangibles difficult to assess. In any case, few of the local doctors had any direct contact with the hospital. Most of their feelings about the hospital were necessarily based on second-hand information.

Some comments by psychiatrists indicate the opinions they had about Crest under Dunn's directorship:

> It became apparent that he was pretty inexperienced to handle a job of this sort, and people he was trying to please, I think, were critical and demanded pretty high standards. I had a feeling that he tried pretty hard, but he simply was too inexperienced. And I think he had his own personal problems that kept interfering. I think

these were the main things. And then, the criticism of him as things went on became pretty much general knowledge; . . . and many people who wouldn't have first hand information would accept the criticism of others they knew pretty well; and I think it snowballed to some extent. There was no question that in the last part, referrals began to drop off pretty severely to the point where, of course, as you probably know, he made them up by taking in adolescents.

And I remember his talking to us at the meeting down at the College Club once. He was talking about his interest in adolescents. And I felt: my gosh—somehow this is his problem.

My impression is that the issue of milieu therapy became really sort of lost among the other things that came up: the attack on Dunn, the feeling that he personally was not doing an adequate job, and the concern about who was going to manage the place, and that sort of thing. . . . Well, his [Clark's] criticisms I think were several, on a variety of levels. They were aimed at Dunn, at the staff, at the treatment that was being done. But the part of Clark's attitude that I think caught on with some of the people in the consulting staff was the disapproval of things in the hospital.

The force, vigor, explosiveness, harshness, and even ferocity of Clark's denunciation stunned many board members. On the one hand, the apparently excessive severity and intensity of Clark's performance appalled them. Some felt sympathetic to Dunn, if only as an underdog. Some of this sympathy may also have stemmed from loyalty to Dr. Crawford, perceived by many as the person who had sponsored and supported Dunn's directorship. On the other hand, board members could scarcely dismiss the opinions of one of the leading psychoanalysts in Columbia, especially since he was one of the founders of Crest. Their confidence in Dunn suffered a severe blow; and they began to wonder about Crest in general. Since their opinions of Crest had been based substantially on Dunn's reports, and they had accepted these reports partly because Dunn was presumed to have the support of the local psychiatric community, the whole foundation of their functioning as a board was shaken.

The reactions of two members of the board to Clark's attack are reflected in the following descriptions:

> I think they definitely were aligned on George [Dunn's] side. It may have raised questions in their minds, but I think that Dr. Clark really cooked his own goose with this silly—it was intemperate; I mean, everything he said was just sort of wild, he really was insulting, and it was quite a meeting. I mean we all sat there, just the sweat pouring off of us, everyone really very angry and yet realizing that here was this terrible gap between the community psychiatrists and the hospital and we had to deal with somebody, and here he was. That was a bad one. . . . And the awful part of it was that you see I felt too that George shouldn't be the director, but I felt it for entirely different reasons. And when Clark came in—you know how you do— I mean somebody hits below the belt and immediately you're going to try to go to the defense of the guy that's getting clobbered. And you sort of forget that, well, some of what he says may be right, but the way he said it was just absolutely unpardonable—it really was.

> When I heard some of the things that Clark allegedly had said and done with regard to George Dunn, I was extremely upset, I had no way of evaluating these statements or his actions. I observed that there were some people who felt as strongly about Dr. Clark as he felt about Dr. Dunn, and here again, who was right? We didn't know, and still don't know. . . . When we did hear that there were, certainly, to put it mildly, differences between the hospital, the medical director, and the psychiatric community, or parts of the psychiatric community, outside the hospital, that were becoming very opposed to one another, this was very upsetting.

The intensity of the reactions of many of the members of the board is understandable. The board was dependent upon professional evaluations of the institution for which it was responsible. The lay members of the board did not know how to determine whether the hospital was running well therapeutically, or failing. They did not know how to evaluate the professional ability of the doctors, including the medical director. There were no satisfactory ways even of determining the number of "cures." At the same time, the board members had to have some idea about the quality of the hospital. They needed to know how well it was functioning in order to be able to approach the community effectively and with confidence in the value of the hospital; in order to judge whether to support a medical director; in order to evaluate long-range policies of the hospital which would have financial implications and implications for the hospital's relationship to the community.

Obviously, the major source for the needed evaluation was from psychiatrists, those on the board, on the hospital staff, and in the community. The board had to accept the judgment of these experts. Any severe disagreement among the psychiatrists about the hospital would be devastating to the board members.

The board was to confront more difficulty. First, in September, 1957, Dr. Dunn submitted his letter of resignation to the board, "for compelling personal reasons." The number of referrals to Crest from the Columbia area had dropped. Although there were other factors, it seems certain that Dr. Clark's attack on the hospital was central to the loss of referrals. Dr. Clark's influence was great; his Columbia Clinic had been the major source of referrals to Crest. As a consequence of the drop in referrals, the hospital balance sheet again went into the red during the last year of Dunn's administration. The board became much more concerned with the details of running the hospital, seeking ways to obtain money and generally to economize. The hospital census was sustained somewhat by referrals of adolescents to the hospital from outside the Columbia area. Thus, the policy of specializing in adolescents, initially embarked upon in order to enhance the hospital, now helped to sustain it.

In any case, the combination of Clark's attack, Dunn's resignation, the split in the psychiatric community, its general criticism of Dunn and Crest, the drop in the rate of referrals, and the ensuing financial problems, were cumulatively disastrous in their effects upon the board. The board had relied upon the experts to evaluate the hospital; now the experts disagreed, and, if anything, were negative. Even the businessmen's yardsticks of census and balance sheets produced discouraging results. The grand vision of the hospital collapsed with nothing to sustain it. The negative verdict of a group of psychiatrists was therefore a catastrophe.

CHAPTER SIX

The Failure
of Leadership:
The Consultants

George Dunn left Crest in June, 1958. No permanent medical director had been found in the six-month interim since Dunn's announcement of his resignation. The only person available who could be considered as qualified to fill in as acting director was James Dale, the staff psychiatrist who had the longest experience at Crest.

When the Board of Trustees offered the acting directorship to Dr. Dale, at first he refused. He was not interested in a position that was primarily administrative, and he considered leaving the hospital rather than accepting the job. However, the Board of Trustees brought strong pressure to bear on him. Probably because of his devotion to Crest and because of its dilemma, he accepted in July, 1958. He made it clear that he did not want the position permanently, and that he would stay in it only long enough to give the Board of Trustees a chance to find another man.

The board was faced with an acute problem of leadership. The acting director was poorly qualified for the position and reluctant to accept it. Of the leadership group at the hospital, no other psychiatrist except Dale remained. In the interim between

Dunn's announcement of his resignation, and before Dale assumed his new responsibilities, Dr. William Plant had departed. As acting director, Dale withdrew from his leadership and educational activities with the nursing and aide staff, and devoted himself to the administrative aspects of his job and to psychotherapy.

In search of needed professional leadership, the board again had to turn to the consultant psychiatrists. The board had begun to make overtures to the consultants in order to establish a closer relationship with them at a meeting on February 28, 1958, a little over two months after Dunn had announced his intention of leaving. At this meeting, the trustees decided to attempt to clarify the role and functions of the consulting staff, with their assitance. On May 28, 1958, the board voted to request that members of the consulting staff put in "definite time periods" at the hospital, with compensation, to help with the burdens of the hospital.

Some of the psychiatrists were quite cynical about the board's turning to the consultants for help at this time. One of them observed, "Only when Crest was on the skids did the board turn for help. You couldn't stop the direction; you could only slow it down." During Dunn's administration, the consulting staff had become isolated from the day-to-day operation of the hospital, and from the Board of Trustees. Dunn's early request for psychoanalysts to participate in the training program at the hospital had not been pushed. Clark's decision to cut off referrals to the hospital from the Columbia Clinic had further isolated the hospital from the local psychiatric community. The younger psychiatrists who treated hospital patients were unwilling to send patients to Crest where, although they could continue to see patients in psychotherapy, they could not direct the patients' hospital experience. Many of them felt that this resulted in a loss of income which they could ill afford.

During Dunn's administration, the Board of Trustees had not turned to the consultants for advice or guidance. Partly, this was owing to the presence of two or three psychiatrists on the board—Crawford, Carpenter, a psychoanalyst and partner in Crawford's clinic, who had been interested in and involved with Crest for many years, and Waters—to whom the board might turn for guidance on professional matters. More importantly, the board had had confidence in Dunn.

The consultant staff had continued to meet regularly. Occasionally, clinical papers were read and discussed at these meetings. Some members reported later that they continued the meetings primarily as a way of socializing with professional colleagues. No clear role for the group with regard to the hospital had been defined, and the consultants felt useless and impotent.

The board members were aware of this isolation. Some of them thought that it was useless to turn to the consultants since they were divided among themselves. One person who joined the board late in Dunn's administration was not aware of the existence of the consulting staff for six months of his membership. To be sure, a representative of the consulting staff was supposed to attend the meetings of the board, but only five of the twelve board meetings from May, 1957, to May, 1958, had been so attended; and only one of the six meetings from October, 1957, to May, 1958.

Gradually the frequency of the meetings of the consultants declined. Finally, the question whether the consulting staff should continue to exist was raised. This occurred after Dunn had submitted his resignation, but while he was still functioning as director. A representative of the consultants to the trustees, who had attended one board meeting, suggested at a consultant staff meeting that "if the consulting staff is serving no definite purpose and has no definite functions, maybe it should be disbanded." Full consideration of this suggestion was postponed to the next meeting.

A special meeting of the consulting staff was called on June 6, 1958, to continue the discussion. The consultants defined a function for themselves. The minutes read:

> Part of the current dissatisfaction lay with the fact that there is lacking a clear understanding of the position of the consulting staff in the selection of a new medical director. It was generally felt that the Board of Trustees be

made aware of the views of the consulting staff in this matter.

A meeting was held between a committee representing the consultants and the Board of Trustees. They agreed that a consultant committee would meet regularly with the president of the board to work on methods for fostering a more effective working relationship between the board and the consultants. At the July 18, 1958, meeting of the consultants, a committee of three members was formed, with Clark as chairman. It was emphasized that this committee would attend board meetings and keep members of the consulting staff informed. At first, Dr. Clark met only with the chairman of the trustees; but, as the two groups moved closer, Clark attended the November 28 and December 19 meetings of the Board of Trustees.

The unhealed rift in the psychiatric community was having an important effect on this maneuvering. At the time of Dunn's departure, there were two psychiatrists who were full members of the Board of Trustees: Crawford and Carpenter, both in the same clinic. (Dr. Crawford resigned from the board in April, 1957, but did not join the consultant staff.) Dr. Dale was in didactic analysis with Dr. Crawford. The Columbia Clinic was not represented on the board. On the other hand, the consultant staff was dominated by psychiatrists from the Columbia Clinic. Thus, the Board of Trustees and the consulting staff represented the two opposed sides in the psychiatric community. The controversy did not affect every member of the consultant staff; the younger and newer members, analytic candidates themselves, were not particularly involved in the split.

Because of this rift, the efforts of the senior consultants to establish closer ties with the Board of Trustees inevitably took the form of a power struggle between the Columbia Clinic group and those loyal to Dr. Crawford, with the board in a subordinate position. During the fall of 1958, the liaison between the board and the consulting staff functioned with only moderate success. On January 16, at a meeting of the consultants, one psychiatrist who was in a liaison position complained that the board was still not apprised of all of the motions passed by the consultants.

Clark and the other two psychiatrists were present for the January 23, 1959, meeting of the Board of Trustees. The minutes of this meeting report: "There was a general discussion of hospital operations at Crest. Dr. Clark among others mentioned items that in his estimation contributed to the current difficulties." This rather bland statement covered an explosion. Dr. Clark had presented his interpretation of the clinical situation at the hospital. But again many members of the Board of Trustees reacted more to his manner of presentation—which was evidently fiery—than to the validity of his criticism. One board member commented:

> Clark was there, and he was almost childish in insulting Dale at a meeting; and as a result we felt that Clark should not represent the consulting staff. . . . Some of the board members felt he was trying to undermine Crest for reasons about which we didn't know. That was the definite impression. (Did this disturb the confidence that the board members had in Crest?) No, it disturbed the confidence they had in Clark.

Clark described this meeting as follows:

> Well, I did make the point at this meeting, that as a board, they needed very much to have some orientation—talks about basic psychological concepts—so that they would know what they were talking about. Because the level of board talk was still: We want to get these poor people and help them; we want to get these poor schizophrenics out of the rain and get them well. Very uneducated sort of talk. And I, about two years before that—John Carpenter and Don Waters were on the board, and they were supposed to have been the psychiatric consultants to the board, being members of the board, and I don't know how much they had done. But I heard Don Waters talking, and they didn't say anything that made any sense to me, very much, and John was quite ambivalent whether to step in or not . . . anyway I started giving them hell.

The trustees, "by unanimous vote" of the executive committee, asked Dr. Clark to resign from the consulting staff because his "difference of opinion with the board and [his] method of approach in discussing these differences has a detrimental effect on the freedom of the members to act." Dr. Clark resigned from the consulting staff, writing to the trustees that he had already reached a decision to resign because "the combination of the Board of Trustees and myself is certainly not a productive combination."

The consultants used this episode as a basis for their attempts to have a greater voice in the affairs of the Board of Trustees. The minutes of a special meeting of the consultants held on February 27, 1959, reveal this:

> Dr. Clark was asked to give an account of his resignation from the consulting staff which was requested by the Board of Trustees. Before he spoke to the consulting staff, the secretary read two letters. One was a letter addressed to Mr. Bond, president of the Board, the other to Dr. Crow from Dr. Clark submitting his resignation from the consulting staff. Dr. Clark reviewed the proceedings at the January meeting of the Board of Trustees. . . .

He was present during the early part of the discussion, and then left. The consultants agreed that:

> It was generally felt that there was a lack of protocol in how the board handled the resignation. But this seemed to be part of a larger and more chronic problem dealing with the absence of adequate communication between the consulting staff and the Board of Trustees. This led once again to the question of the purpose and function of the consulting staff and the fact the consulting staff has hardly been used in a consulting capacity, certainly not as a group.
>
> Discussion then centered around an attempt to get some understanding of the present difficulties and precarious situation of the Crest Hospital. Some explanations were offered regarding the inadequate medical directors of the

past as well as various descriptive adjectives with regard to the Board of Trustees. Dr. Forte offered the suggestion of a possible change in the structure and philosophy of the hospital so that it would be more open to the consultants in handling their own cases. He also thought that 4 to 6 weeks of hospital treatment rather than 2 years would be a more realistic objective.

After some discussion of this point Dr. Cabot stated that with regard to the purpose of this meeting, we should ask the Board of Trustees why they took this unprecedented action related to Dr. Clark without informing the consulting staff. Dr. Hagen made the motion that the executive committee of the consulting staff request a meeting with a committee of the Board of Trustees to discuss 1) the resignation of Dr. Clark, 2) the problem of communication between the consulting staff and Board of Trustees, and 3) how the present difficulties can be improved.

[It was decided] to instruct the committee to ask the Board of Trustees for a meeting in which the total membership of each group would come together to discuss the various problems.

On that same night, the Board of Trustees met and voted to invite Dr. Crawford to again become a member of the board. He accepted. Dr. Crawford's role on the board is well described by him:

> There was no official differentiation between professional and lay members of the board. Any member of the board could hold any office or serve on any committee. In practice, however, individuals were sometimes elected to the board for particular purposes; e.g., someone to take over public relations or someone to advise as to architectural and landscaping matters. Psychiatrists on the board inevitably served as psychiatric consultants to the board in matters of policy and in selection of key personnel at the hospital. This, however, never prevented members of the

board from talking with psychiatrists not on the board or, later, from having the consulting staff represented at meetings of the board. The usefulness or influence of any psychiatrist with respect to the Board of Trustees was a factor of his total personality, not of his elective or appointive position.

Both Dr. Crawford, to whom the board had been in the habit of turning for advice, and the senior members of the consulting staff were establishing closer ties to the board. A clash was inevitable; the senior consultants were determined to end what they perceived as Dr. Crawford's domination of the board.

At this moment the Board of Trustees faced another severe problem, a financial crisis. After Dunn's departure, particularly as a consequence of the abrupt cessation of referrals from the Columbia Clinic, the census at the hospital had been decreasing. In January, 1959: "Mr. Kippen, treasurer, stated in his report that it was now necessary to change the budget inasmuch as expenses were up and income down in all departments. He was to report further on changes made." And in February, 1959, "Mr. Hanson reported with the treasurer, Mr. Kippen, informing the Board of a $7000 loss for January with an average census of 21.9 patients. Mr. Kippen stressed the seriousness of the financial crisis. . . . There was general discussion of fund-raising as the only alternative to an increased census."

The situation reached a climax in March, 1959, precipitated, in part, by the continuing drop in the census. From an average population of twenty-seven in October, 1958, the census had dropped markedly to eighteen, the lowest monthly average in more than seven years. In January, too, the problem of the leadership situation was made even more acute by Dr. Dale's announcement of his resignation. He was to stay until June.

To solve both the financial problem and the problem of replacing Dale, the trustees turned more actively and urgently to the consultants. They attempted to increase the referrals to Crest by making it a more attractive place for local psychiatrists to refer patients. On March 12, 1959, the executive committee of

the board met, at their request with the executive committee of
the consulting staff. The board members, financially frantic,
raised a question they had heard periodically from some consultants:

> There was a discussion as to the possibility of having
> perhaps three local psychiatrists alternate as medical di-
> rector which in turn would probably have to be coupled
> with the right of local psychiatrists to treat their patients
> at Crest. Dr. Jones advised that there was a difference of
> opinion among members of the consulting staff as to
> whether such a procedure would be practical. All of the
> representatives of the consulting staff appeared to believe
> that the Crest philosophy, milieu treatment, has a place
> of value in this area.

As the financial crisis continued, the executive committee of
the Board of Trustees considered a variety of solutions:

> (a) obtaining donations; (b) cutting down the staff and
> operations to a hospital equal in size to the census (the
> census had dropped to 17 about a week ago and is now 20
> with the chances that it will be 21); (c) consideration of
> the possibility of local psychiatrists as alternating medical
> director with patients being treated by local psychiatrists;
> (d) an emergency meeting (two days later) of the Board
> to take action.

The administrator was asked to prepare, for the emergency meeting, a rough estimate as to whether and how the operation could
be cut to a fifteen- or twenty-bed hospital.

On March 27, 1959, the Board of Trustees and consulting staff
met separately and then jointly. At their separate meeting the
consultants decided to make two proposals to the board: first,
that no psychiatrist be a member of the board; second, that a
committee of six from the consulting staff be selected by the
consultants with the approval of the Board of Trustees to advise
the latter on professional matters. That night the board accepted
the proposal with regard to the committee of six. Four of the six

psychiatrists chosen for the committee were from the Columbia Clinic. One non-Columbia Clinic psychiatrist, John Carpenter, who had been on both the Board of Trustees and consulting staff, felt obliged to resign from the new committee.

> I thought a psychiatrist was needed on the board, because the board didn't have the foggiest notion of a psychiatric set up, and I thought if only for information it was important that a psychiatrist be on the board. I was sore as hell that night, frankly, and I did it largely in anger.
>
> You see, Tom [Crawford] had just gone on the board when this was promulgated, and it was proposed at that meeting at the Athletic Club that there be no more psychiatrists on. And I thought that this was probably directed, was aimed partly at Tom, and I just couldn't see how it would function otherwise, after having spent an inordinate amount of time at board meetings and seeing that people didn't know how things worked. I mean they had no way of evaluating, well, for example, getting a medical director. . . . And it seemed awfully false to me for all of a sudden the consulting staff to say O.K. now we'll come in and we'll show you how things should be done after years and years and years of doing nothing.

At a meeting one week later, the board accepted the consultants' request that no psychiatrists be on the board. The trustees, however, were concerned with the makeup of the consultant committee. At the board's April meeting, it resolved to use the committee as "adviser on professional matters." The minutes continue:

> However, Dr. Thomas [a local surgeon] was appointed to confer with the consulting staff committee to inform them that the Board felt it would be better that the committee be balanced somewhat so that a majority thereof would not be from the Columbia Clinic. This

would avoid any feeling among psychiatrists that the Columbia Clinic dominated.

There is no evidence that the consultants considered the board's concern. In any case, the committee of five, four from the Columbia Clinic, was not changed.

With Dunn's resignation, the search for a new director had become a prime objective of the board. This search, to be characterized by trials and tribulations, began actively in September 27, 1957, while Dunn was the lame-duck director. The board's first move was to authorize its professional committee, chaired by Dr. Thomas, to look for a new director. The board asked Dunn to give the committee a list of qualifications for a new director. By November, Dr. Crawford reported that he had found three potential candidates, one an eminently qualified man. Thomas opened negotiations with him, and on January 31, 1958, the Board of Trustees made an offer. This offer was refused.

At this January meeting, Dr. Carpenter raised the question of the role of the consultants in the selection of a director. Thomas was instructed to contact the president of the consulting staff. Thomas' contacts with the consultants were apparently not satisfactory to them. In June, 1958, the consultants defined a role for themselves and the Board of Trustees accepted their offer to help in the selection of a director; no new director had been located through the board's own efforts, and the response to notices of the opening in official psychiatric news bulletins had not been good.

In the fall of 1958, negotiations with another highly qualified man were launched. The consultants were involved in these negotiations, as Thomas reported both to them and to the board. However, by March, 1959, nothing had come of all efforts. The reasons were various: lack of interest in administrative work among psychiatrists; the poor financial state of the hospital at the time; the relatively low salary offered; disagreement about hospital policy.

The new committee of five psychiatrists took on as their responsibility the task of finding a new medical director. The board welcomed this: more than a year had passed since Dunn's resignation and no director had been found; there were serious financial difficulties; and Dale had tendered his resignation. The situation was "desperate." A consultant stated:

All I can remember is that the situation was presented to us as desperate, by the board and by the hospital—"do something, do something, do something"—and we were under that pressure.

Some board members felt that they were in no position to evaluate the professional qualifications of potential medical directors, nor even to find candidates.

I think that those of us who were laymen on the board had quite some time before that decided that we didn't know a darn thing about how to pick a psychiatrist to run an institution, that this simply and clearly had to be in the hands of other people who were familiar with the entire field as we were not.

The shift from the board to the consultants represented more than a shift in personnel; it was also a shift in approach. Thomas had been quite concerned about the administrative ability and qualifications of any new medical director. He had been concerned, in addition, about how acceptable the new director would be to the personnel at the hospital. This latter consideration, while shared by the hospital staff, was not shared by powerful members of the consulting staff nor by all members of the board. Thomas comments:

Some of the members of the consulting staff, I think, felt antagonistic towards some of the personnel at the hospital, and felt it ridiculous that they would have anything to say about who would be the big chief; and I had difficult times with consulting staff members at board meetings, and had to take some ridicule.

The controversy over whether to check with the hospital staff reflected other subtle but significant differences in approach to the directorship. Thomas felt that administrative ability was very important. Others felt that stature as a psychoanalyst was more important.

Dr. Crawford supported Thomas' view and submitted a memo to the president of the board:

> . . . The director, the executive or the chief of staff—whatever his title—in these situations needs an even greater self-confidence, firmer touch and a more imaginative understanding of the subtle operations of "the personal equation" than, say, the head of a department store or the president of a bank. In a psychiatric hospital, the emotional impact of disturbed patients on staff makes every hour of every day seem more nerve-wracking than a threatened congressional investigation in the State Department, and doctors may tend to take it out on nurses, nurses on aides, aides on each other and so on *ad infinitum*. I have been told that a colleague has asserted that anyone who can successfully treat schizophrenic patients can be a successful medical director. This, in my opinion, is nonsense. The germ of truth in this assertion arises from the fact that patients sometimes need firmness and always need consistency, and that the same is true of hospital staffs. Despite such similarities, management and treatment differ in many of the ways that groups and individuals differ. Besides, a medical director has also to deal realistically with the Board and to do an adequate public relations job. It is my opinion that the Crest Board is better qualified to judge a prospective medical director as to his administrative and leadership qualifications than are most psychiatrists.
>
> Beyond these considerations is the fact that the analyzed medical director is better able to understand the needs of both patients and staff, and better able to deal with them.
>
> The question has been asked: Does the medical director have to be a training analyst? The answer, in my opinion, is "no."

On the other hand, Drs. Clark and Crane of the Columbia Clinic placed more emphasis upon the medical director's ability and experience as an analyst and as a therapist. One member of the board commented on Clark's position:

> The thing that I will never forget is Sid Clark saying at one of these meetings that it was clear to him that if you got a top-flight psychiatrist, that *ipso facto* you would get a top administrator.

Another said:

> There were statements made, that you don't have to know anything about administration, if you are a good analyst that all follows; and some people actually made that statement, that we don't need to evaluate that because anybody who is a good analyst can be a good hospital director, and we don't have to worry, then, about these others. Those statements were made.

In spite of the arguments in favor of the salience of administrative qualifications, the Board of Trustees had to choose someone who would be acceptable as a professional peer by the senior psychoanalysts. Experience with the previous directors had convinced the board of this.

> It was the final evolution of discussion, with not necessarily the consulting staff, but the psychiatric group in town, that an analyst must be secured; and it was the board's desire to have a man who was of such stature that the consulting staff wouldn't be knifing him.

In May, the committee finally found the man. Dr. Thomas Doren had very good recommendations. He was an analyst. He had done therapy with psychotics, and had taught at several universities. He was an amiable, steady, stable person. He did not, however, have hospital administrative experience.

> Actually, those of us on the consulting staff reacted very favorably to Doren from the very beginning. . . . We liked him; we felt quite confident in his ability to pull the thing together.

Board members stated:

> We felt that a professional committee should certainly
> select the new medical director; and we had great hope in
> Dr. Doren when he was proposed, and when he came out
> to Columbia. We met him, and his records indicated a
> man of very high capability; and I believe many thought
> that this would be the solution.

> We were so jubilant at having such a strong recom-
> mendation, and I think, as I recall, we had a good recom-
> mendation from Topeka. I think Tom Crawford said,
> this looks like the answer.

Dr. Doren suffered a coronary, and his convalescence delayed
his arrival at the hospital. But the need for a saviour was strong
enough to overcome apprehensions.

> I think we were so pleased at having . . . solved it, that
> we couldn't care less if he had two heart attacks—we
> would have kept him and been pleased with it.

The absence of leadership at the hospital, the lack of a strong
medical director, forced the board to look to the consulting staff
for help with administrative problems. The same thing occurred
with clinical problems at the hospital. The consultants were
called on for help, first through supervision of psychotherapy.

In prior years local psychoanalysts had been supervising some
of the psychotherapists at the hospital. This had begun as part of
the regular training of resident psychiatrists. After Dunn's departure, in response to the board's request for help, the consultants decided that all psychotherapists at the hospital should
be supervised. There had been four supervisors; Dale attempted
to recruit two more, but did not formally work through the
consulting staff. On June 6, 1958, however, a suggestion was
made at a meeting of the consulting staff that all requests for
consultants' time as supervisors be channeled through the president of the consulting staff.

In response, Dr. Dale wrote to the president of the consulting
staff. He noted that, "The matter had been quite obscure to me

in many ways." After describing the current supervision situation, he continued:

> I deeply regret any misunderstanding which has occurred around the supervision need. I believe it is quite possible that some of my initial moves in this matter were very misunderstood. It would also seem that the situation of the consulting staff at a time when I first approached potential supervisors was somewhat misunderstood by me. I had seriously thought that their disbanding was imminent.
>
> In contrast to the discussion as to whether or not the consulting staff had any real purpose in regard to Crest I must say that this matter of supervision is a way in which our consultants can be most helpful to both the individual supervisees and to myself. Naturally such help is in turn very significant to the hospital as a functioning treatment unit. Thanks again.

At this point both the hospital and the board were subordinate to the consulting staff. The acting medical director was plainly subordinate to the senior members of the consulting staff. He was a junior person, just beginning his analytic training, which he regarded as quite important. He was a reluctant director and avoided action that might antagonize the consultants. His attitude was very different from Dunn's, who disagreed with his analytic superiors and did not attend regularly the courses in psychoanalysis.

The consulting staff, in their attempt to be constructive and helpful to the hospital, tended to deal with the hospital and the board as if they were patients. One young consultant stated:

> The board was being talked about [by the senior consultants] like it was a collective patient; this is bad treatment for the board. The board wasn't a patient or a child. And this idea of "treating" people and "treating" the hospital staff, or "treating" the hospital somehow began to be talked about. I mean, this is what made me kind of sick. . . . During this time, I was perturbed a

few times by the way some of the consulting staff talked
about the hospital people. Maybe they didn't talk in any
more derogatory way than I've just been talking about:
the cult and so on; but it seemed to me . . . an attitude
of we ought to run this thing the way it ought to be run
and straighten these guys out, rather than saying now
here's a structure that is having a hard time and let's see
if we can somehow revitalize it or give it strength, but
keeping its own structure.

The committee of five consultants set to work in March to
help administer the hospital until a new director could take over.
They quickly appointed one of their members, Dr. Morton, a
Columbia Clinic psychoanalyst, as acting medical director of the
hospital, since Morton had said he had a little time available.
The choice of Dr. Morton as director clearly indicated the attitude of the committee toward the hospital and its problems. It is
significant that Dr. Morton was the one and only member of the
committee who had not had any extended experience in hospitals, let alone as a hospital administrator. Three of the committee members had extensive experience as hospital administrators.
Morton's appointment was related to the attitude that the "sick"
hospital needed an analyst. It is obvious that the involvement of
the committee in helping Crest was not very great. Dr. Morton
said he had some time available. He came out to Crest twice a
week, from seven to nine in the morning. One consultant
summed it up nicely: "It was very generous of him. He was the
only one who would get up at seven in the morning when he
didn't have to and go running out there."

The absence of strong leadership at the hospital had powerful
effects on the morale and effectiveness of the hospital staff.
Morale had begun to decline during Dunn's administration, but
it reached alarming proportions a half-year or more following his
departure. The essential reason was the lack of leadership. Dale's
lack of enthusiasm was obvious to the board and to the consultants.

I don't think James Dale was guy who could step in and
be a real hospital administrator. He's a fine guy, but he's

not the type to meet the public and carry a cause, you might say.

He talked with such a soft voice, you could hardly hear him. And he could never make up his mind; he just wasn't the kind of a person to run an institution.

In Dale's devotion to the administrative details of running the hospital, he withdrew from the close supportive communications he had enjoyed with the ward staff. He no longer was particularly interested in the classes for aides, and he became much less accessible to the ward staff. His withdrawal was exceedingly important, since many of the ward staff had come to depend on Dale for guidance and support. Dunn and Plant, the other psychiatrists who were "Crest," were gone. The following statements illustrate the reactions of the staff. The director of nurses, Ruth Nichols, said:

Once a week we had these ward conferences where the doctors attended. James didn't generally come, he had too many things to do, he couldn't attend, although I thought he didn't want to. I felt that if he really wanted to he would find time. . . . And I don't think the caliber of them was the same; and, boy, I can't tell you exactly why I think they were different except I don't think people really hashed out things much. . . . They were never the old kind of conferences where people were enthused and there would be spontaneous little stories where they would talk about what was happening with so and so. They were very formal kinds of things compared to what they had been, much more formal. And then somebody would say, oh well, we can't talk about that patient, that's Dr. Dale's and then he would be passed on.

A recreational therapist stated:

In my thinking he had been one of the warmest—I loved Jim Dale [before he was director]—I had so much respect for him, for his quietness, for his strength, for his interest. [After he became director] he didn't seem to care. . . . Now, why, I don't know; but . . . I think he

stopped thinking Crest was very good, and I certainly had
that feeling.

An aide stated:

> He didn't seem to be there so much. He seemed to be
> always away, I don't know. I realize a medical director
> has to do more things than just be a therapist to his
> particular group of patients. But yet, when you'd see
> him, he was quite conscientious about his patients, he
> would still come down to read their charts and call us up
> and say: tell me what happened last night, I want to
> know—this type of thing. But he just didn't seem to have
> the time. I don't think he took on any more patients, any
> new ones.

Not only was Dale withdrawn, but he tended to be more severe on the hospital staff than the previous directors or he himself had been before:

> I don't think I've ever been criticized by a doctor as I was
> by James. Nothing was right that I did or the aides or
> nurses did—it was just absolute complete turnabout. Be-
> fore he had . . . well, people could make mistakes, and
> they made mistakes, and were forgiven. They were not
> forgiven at this time.

However, some communication between the ward staff and the
medical staff continued during this period. There were four
other psychiatrists, two of whom were residents. The older, more
experienced ward staff felt they still were able to communicate
well with many of the doctors, although this varied greatly from
doctor to doctor. The new ward staff, however, did not feel quite
so free to communicate. But it was the older ones who were more
disturbed by Dale's withdrawal.

Meanwhile, the professional staff were having their difficulties.
With the departure and withdrawal of the core leadership group,
the earlier integration had disappeared.

> That was the time, remember, when we had a series of
> monthly staff meetings that were kind of sad: Ruth was

> crying, Miss Simmons was kind of sitting on the floor and
> throwing her legs out—real stupid, you know.

The highly integrated group which had met during Dunn's administration, and which had maintained the hospital during the
last years of his administration, had fallen apart. Furthermore,
there was friction between Dale and the director of nurses.

> Ruth and him were having tremendous difficulties at this
> time. Ruth would have appointments with him that she
> would forget; he'd forget; she would come up to my office
> and be so angry she would cry; he didn't know what
> happened. That was chaotic, just chaotic. Nobody at the
> helm, really, for quite a long time.

The director of nurses also had difficulties with the residents;
matters not too different from those which had existed in the
previous years of the hospital; but they came to a head now, as
the result of the serious problem the hospital faced in dealing
with the adolescent patients. Nichols' experience with such patients was limited. In the face of this new situation, it was still
her task to orient incoming residents to the "Crest way." Friction between herself and the residents was greatly aggravated by
this test of her role as leader.

> I think that my impression always was: well, maybe she
> has much more experience than any of the rest of these
> younger people there, and she really could do this better,
> but she was limited by the fact that she was a nurse and
> we were physicians, and we had the responsibility, and
> therefore there was disagreement. And I can recall a staff
> meeting about that time in which I was trying to instruct
> the staff and discuss with them—work out their feelings
> and concerns about this. Instead of the usual thing that I
> had been used to in other situations, where it was just staff
> and I, there was somebody sitting there, chewing their
> fingernails and shaking her head and making all sorts of
> subtle communications that this was all wrong, it should
> be done differently. And so I sensed that I was rather
> powerless in this position as far as this; I mean, anything

about the group attitude and carrying out my role as physician and responsibilities towards my patients.

The discord among the staff, the departure of many of the leadership group in the hospital staff, the withdrawal of interest in the ward staff by the new acting director, the general lack of fire and enthusiasm in the leadership of the hospital, all combined to lead to a great decline in the morale of the ward staff. They no longer had the sense that Crest was the tremendously effective and significant institution it used to be. The ward staff felt that no one was interested in their work. They believed that the doctors had a very low evaluation of the significance of milieu therapy, and the work of the ward personnel in general. The mood of the ward staff was described by some of its members:

> I think hardly an awareness that they were supposed to have the therapeutic efficiency; they had ward duties, and you saw that they got their baths and they got their dinners; refreshments got around, you tried to spend so much time with each patient, but I don't think too much awareness or concern about the fact that I'm in a therapy situation.
>
> The growing apart of people; they worked together at the hospital without dissension particularly, but an apathy, a not-caring, and certainly not a fraternization like I had known it. Now some of that I think was me, because I looked to return to exactly the same type of close-knit place that I had left, and found instead a strangeness. Now part of this was because I was gone and I had grown away. But I think it existed, because I talked with other people about it, and they said, "Yes, it happened." I mean, old-timers, you know, Ruth and Jane and some of the people that had known the way the hospital was; we all felt that it was no longer a really dedicated group of people. Nobody would say whether or not that was healthy or not, because in a way a lot of us who worked at Crest—and certainly I would head the list, Crest was a very big part of my life—and it was for a lot of

people that worked there. And whether this is good or bad, I don't know, but it was true, and I think that it stopped being this for a lot of people, stopped being as important, and they didn't work as hard at being interested in the hospital.

In the last couple of years, the feeling is different; different kinds of people felt demoralization and lethargy and a lack of real interest in patients and patient problems and patients as people.

The absence of any general impetus of dynamic movement in the hospital and the impression that ward work was not particularly important caused a loss of self-esteem among the ward staff. They no longer could feel that they had status, either through identification with Crest or because of the importance of their work. Thus they no longer experienced any great motivation to cooperate for the benefit of the total institution. Individuals became more interested in their particular jobs or niches. Sometimes these limited interests centered around the performance of certain routine duties, sometimes around the patient to whom one was assigned. There was also a breakdown of the close-knit social groupings among the ward staff. Gatherings at the local tavern after work declined. The old aides began to look down upon the newer, less experienced aides.

When I first started, as I said before, we always used to stop for a beer after shift, and this may sound like a small thing, but it was an important thing, and some of us always did. And at this point we stopped doing that anymore. Oh, once in awhile somebody would nag, and we would do it, but it wasn't a wanted type of thing, it was a forced thing. Of course, part of the reason for that was maybe feeling that we were carrying more of a load than we could handle, that we needed more medical staff. Part of it was the fact that some of us who had been there a long time, had started when we were single, now we were married, and we had children, we had to get home; all these factors figured in. But still there wasn't this same feeling of comradeship among us in the evening shift as there had been before.

I think during that time, somehow, I became increasingly aware of the lack of communication. One of the things I noted when I came back to Crest was that the departments didn't work as well together, by that I mean, for one thing something happened, aides started owning their patients, a different system of assignments had come along then, they had assigned certain patients to certain aides and then these aides worked day in and day out with the same patients; well, they became owners of patients, I mean, this was my patient, the aide said, and the patient said this is my aide.

Tremendous detail as far as what chores; who empties waste baskets, who washes glasses, and carries linen down, and a lot of irritation between shifts: you didn't wash all your glasses last shift, and we had to wash them for you and by gosh we're not coming on the ward tonight until you do—and we found some of the waste baskets unemptied.

There was the sudden growth of concern about hierarchy among the staff. The older aides felt superior to the newer ones; and some aides envied the status of the nurses. More nurses had been hired in proportion to aides than previously, in an effort to compensate for the apparent poor quality of the newer aides. This influx of new nurses threatened the aides who often did the same work as the nurses, yet received less pay. The large number of nurses led to the rise of status problems among the nurses themselves.

It seemed to me a sort of scurrying around to get, on the part of certain members of the hierarchy, better job classifications. In the beginning we just had a superintendent of nurses, Ruth Nichols, and, lo and behold, all of a sudden we had an assistant superintendent of nurses, and, lo and behold, we had someone that was designated as clinical supervisor. And it seemed to me to be kind of a rush

but a concern amongst the RN's about who was going to
be officially the charge nurse on this ward and the charge
nurse on that ward and the night supervisor.

Social gatherings at this time began to be tinged with what
some called a "sick" quality. Two aides described a Hallowe'en
party that year:

> I was living with Roger Adams at the time and I at-
> tended part of the real bizarre, hard to explain really,
> almost sort of sick, sick, sick party, and whether it was
> because they had this many sick, sick, sick people on the
> staff or not, I don't know. (There was a lot of hostility?)
> A lot of that. Of course, a lot of it was sparked by a few
> people, I imagine you could say were definitely hostile,
> and still are—I mean, there was somebody that jerked
> everything down in the bathroom, and everything fas-
> tened to the wall. . . . There was one period somebody
> was happily in the kitchen breaking empty bottles over
> the edge of the kitchen sink, and somebody was outside
> throwing bottles at the landlady's back porch; girls liter-
> ally dancing on busted glass with bare feet, and not seem-
> ing to be aware of it, and pretty wild behavior on the
> part of a lot of people. Some people walked in and
> turned around and walked out. (Had any party like that
> occurred before?) No. Maybe wild parties before, quite a
> bit of kicking up their heels, but certainly not this pre-
> vailing mood amongst everybody there. (Do you have
> any ideas why this occurred then?) I think it's probably
> pent up feelings from the hospital situation, that had an
> awful lot to do with it.

> In October, 1958, there was this very large staff party
> at my house. And it turned into a violent violent affair
> where people broke glasses and bottles, and there was a
> brawl, and in fact two divorces started as of that night, a
> couple separated that night. Let's see, which doctors were
> there. Dr. Dale was there, he was treating a girl's foot, she
> had stepped on a broken glass and lacerated her foot.
> And Dr. Preston was there. And everybody, after they

reflected on their own behavior and the behavior of others—in my talk with Dale about this, he felt that the party was simply a symptom of the ills of the hospital, and he felt that it was very interesting and wished that somebody could have been a sober observer. Also, a little before this party, the aides decided to go on strike, and I was one of the leaders of this. We really did feel that we were not getting adequate wages; there had been many promises for a raise but none of them ever came through. And Ruth's reaction to this was almost hysterical. She said that this was not the way that things were done at Crest, and that none of her aides had ever treated her this way before, and she didn't know what was wrong, and if we wanted to get anything done, be reasonable, and on and on. And then she would refuse to talk about it. And it was thought that she would bring it up at a staff conference, but she didn't. Then I made an appointment with Dr. Dale to talk with him about that too. And he thought that the strike was more than just a protest.

The strike never occurred; but the professional staff was shocked that it should even have been contemplated. Representations were made to the director of nurses and the acting medical director that the staff would strike unless wages were raised. On November 28, 1958, Dale reported to the Board of Trustees that sixteen of the aides had asked for a raise. "After considerable discussion, approval was given for a small increase in this category."

The Hallowe'en party was followed by a Christmas party, at which some of the medical staff "necked" with some of the female aides. This behavior did nothing to enhance the stature of the professional staff, nor to raise the morale of the ward staff. One nurse reports:

> I know after that party there was, I remember, this one particular nurse who said that she was really disillusioned and couldn't have the respect for one particular doctor; she was just shocked by his behavior, and she thought that this would definitely influence her attitude toward

him. I mean, his behavior was so bad that she just couldn't believe it, and it just changed her whole attitude to his work and personality.

The low morale of the ward staff, the staff's low level of motivation to be therapeutic, their sagging self-esteem and self-confidence, created hopelessness and anxiety among the patients. One of the aides later described this communication of anxiety:

> I feel that patients always know what goes on. I don't think you can keep anything from them, the explanation of why is pretty simple. I was sitting with a patient early one morning at breakfast time, Saturday morning. You could tell how everybody was feeling by the way they were walking. She saw nothing except the four walls of the room; like a blind person, she was highly attuned to what was going on, and she would say, "Well, Mary [a nurse] is certainly in a gloomy mood this morning," or "What's Nick so goddamn mad about, he'd come clomp, clomping down the hall?" I'm sure there were all kinds of nonverbal forms of communication that would let a patient know that we were anxious about them, ways you wouldn't think of, unless you were a patient.

This downward spiral of confidence culminated in an acute general disturbance, the "adolescent rebellion." Adolescents had been referred to Crest as a consequence of the wish for such patients under Dunn's leadership. At that time, most of the adolescents were considered to be schizophrenic; Crest, it was believed, could treat schizophrenics successfully. By this time, however, the staff considered that most of the adolescents really were afflicted with character disorders, not the sort of cases Crest could best treat.

It is difficult to determine how much of this shift from diagnosing the adolescents as psychotics to diagnosing them as character disorders was an expression of the staff's feeling of hopelessness. In any case, the evidence from our systematic sampling of the patients in the hospital reveals that the adolescents, no less adolescent character disorders, constituted only a small percentage of the patient population during this period.

TABLE 1

Year	Patient Population	Mean Age	Patients Under 20	% Under 20
1950	12	42.6	1	8.3
1951	26	42.0	1	3.8
1952	26	40.1	3	11.0
1953	24	43.4	4	4.0
1954	20	37.3	2	20.0
1955	24	39.0	3	8.0
1956	18	34.7	6	17.0
1957	21	38.9	3	29.0
1958	20	35.5	2	15.0
1959	22	42.0	3	9.0

TABLE 2

Diagnosis—Patients Under 20

Year	% Psychosis	% Psycho- neurosis	% Character Disorder	% Other
1950	100			
1951	100			
1952	100			
1953	100			
1954	50	25	25	
1955	50		50	
1956	66			33
1957	66		33	
1958	66		33	
1959	100			

The percentage of patients who were adolescent was 29 in 1957 (six patients) and 15 (three patients) in 1958. Furthermore, of the adolescents, 66 per cent were schizophrenic rather than character disorders during these years. Thus, objectively, the hospital was not overrun with adolescents, and certainly not with adolescent character disorder persons. The ward staff's fixation on adolescent character disorders was an expression of feelings of inadequacy. The director of nurses later talked of "These gangs of kids—I call them gangs; there were two or three at that time—they felt like twenty-five, you know, when they got going."

Despite their relatively small number, then, the adolescents caused a great deal of difficulty for the staff, especially in areas in which the lack of self-confidence and support among the staff was particularly marked.

> These guys have a way of just picking out the tender spots and pounding away at them. That's sort of an abstract way to put it, but they knew how to work on the aides, they knew which aides to work on, and which areas in which to work. They knew how to upset the hospital. They were past masters at it, and it's really tough to find a whole group of people as a staff who can adequately handle this.

> The whole [recreation] department, the general attitude was that they were not people who would do this controlling, and they asked that aides accompany patients, and they would leave it up to the aide. The aide would say, "Well, you're in charge of this game, not me," and "I can't tell the patient whether he can play on that side of the net or on this side of the net," etc., and, "This is your job." Well, we would have conferences about this and then it would maybe go along but it was never clear cut, it just ended up this way all the time, there was always this battle between nursing personnel and recreation about controls and particularly about the younger kids.

The adolescents often maneuvered or induced others to violate some hospital edict. The manipulators appeared to sense the staff's feelings of inadequacy in controlling patients, and did some controlling themselves. Difficulties arose mostly in the evening and at night when doctors rarely were on the grounds; the ward staff were then particularly vulnerable, as they had little confidence in themselves. The adolescents, seeming to sense this, pressed the staff at their weakest points.

The adolescent patients refused to retire in the evening, and often carried on their revels until three o'clock in the morning. They removed fixtures from the walls and ceilings. Some of them could pick any lock at the hospital and did so repeatedly, one taunting the staff by leaving on the lounge table all the new, recently installed, locks. One night a schizophrenic adolescent attacked an aide by hitting him over the head with a stocking containing a heavy object. Adolescent patients stole other patients' cars and some of the staff's cars were tampered with. One night an adolescent boy climbed up into the rafters of the locked ward, carrying a metal bar with which he threatened the ward staff. The frightened ward staff could not get him down; they called Ruth Nichols who told them to call the police. Eight policemen arrived. One told the boy to come down, and he did—"just like that."

The climactic incident occurred in the lodge, the recreation and living room, in a separate building from the wards. The aide who was on duty that night recalled:

> A bunch of them [three adolescents] had been cutting loose down at the lodge. And I had removed one of them forcibly, had somebody come and get him; I think I had [an aide] who took him back to the west wing. And in about fifteen minutes he [patient] came back. The aide had let him come back, and this made me pretty angry; and of course when he came back, he came back with this wide belt, you know, and the boys then took off their belts, the three of them. . . . But the charge nurse was someone that I didn't feel could help me, and I can remember a pretty tense situation with all the male aides down in the lodge, but not enough to fight the situation, and I suppose probably had we moved in they would have backed down. As I recall it, it ended up with the kids saying they wouldn't go up until midnight, and a stand-off until midnight, at which time they went. And this situation lasted then until midnight; and just about midnight, a couple of minutes to, Dr. Rector [a psychiatric resident] came in, and said how's everything? And the patients said everything's fine, we're just going up. And, "okay, goodnight," and off he went. And this was on a Saturday night. I was pretty griped then. And on Sunday I came to work at four o'clock and it was almost

the same shift that had been on the night before; and I found out that these same patients had been down at the lodge all day, a real goof, that somebody had pretty much let us down during the day. And so I said that I wouldn't have them down there in the evening, and they were then not let out. And it was that night then that they ran away, two of them, and I think that was the same time they took the cash box and stole another patient's car—that was it. And then the kids didn't come back, and a female patient was taken out by her parents, and I felt that this was really a catastrophic event at Crest.

The resultant anxiety was enormous. The staff responded by rejecting the adolescent patients, by getting rid of them. After this last incident a decision was made not to admit more than a limited number of adolescents. Advantage was taken of the fact that of the two leaders of the adolescent rebellion who had escaped the hospital, one refused to return. Shortly after the other was returned to the hospital, a member of the ward staff "inadvertently" helped him to escape.

In retrospect, some of the staff explained the "inadequacy," saying that they had been trained to work primarily with schizophrenic patients rather than character disorders. Moreover, the ward staff felt that the doctors as a group had let them down, had failed to supply the positive, dynamic, strong leadership that was needed.

I can remember feeling that Dr. Preston [a Menninger-trained, new staff psychiatrist] was very protective of [a difficult adolescent] and that it was real hard for me to talk to Dr. Preston about this patient. He used to be one of my real problems down at the lodge, and I think by this time I was lodge aide in the evenings. And I didn't seem to be able to talk to Dr. Preston, or if I did get to him, I didn't seem to get the satisfaction regarding the patient that I felt I needed. I can remember being pretty unhappy with him at the time.

It seemed that the doctors—although Rhodes [a psychiatric resident] did a good job—that they weren't sure of what they wanted to do. There was a trial-and-error basis as far as I could see, and we weren't sure we had nothing to contribute, and I think our most concern was for our own safety, for the safety of the patients. And it reached a point where we just weren't able to handle it; and I think we blamed the doctors for it, we used them as a fall guy.

And the result was that the staff were turning to the professional staff, and in effect what they were saying was, "We have a situation we can't handle. Will you handle it for us?" and the professional staff was saying, "You've got to handle it at the ward level, because you are the ones who are faced with the problem." And the staff felt that they were not being supported, and it sort of wound up into an ever diminishing circle, and the result was a variety of levels of anxiety and insecurity. During these times I feel definitely that staff was not confident. . . . They felt inadequate to handle the ward situation in general. They were, you might say, demoralized and disorganized on some occasions.

They were telling us things that we should do, things that we must do, and trying to give us advice, but we simply couldn't. I don't think we could carry it out. These kids were one jump ahead of us all the time. They had us beaten. I think the doctors were doing as much as they could. I don't know. As a matter of fact, right now I can't remember what we were being asked to do. But the old things with which we had been quite successful, with schizophrenics, and maybe one person like this, or two at a time, didn't seem to work. I think the doctors were as much beside themselves as the ward staff, except that they didn't have to deal with it eight hours—this evening business was just awful.

They [doctors] just couldn't seem to get together on what the problem was and how to deal with it, and it was the lack of confidence, I think, on both parts.

The director of nurses felt that she did not have the background and experience to guide the nursing staff in dealing with adolescents.

> And I remember specifically getting out two books, having them on my desk, and ready for this group so when they came in I could talk something about adolescent problems and how other people were having similar kinds of problems. This was a new problem, and found myself really trying to help these kids theoretically on how to deal with this. . . . But the whole thing, emotionally, we were not ready, staffwise, we were not ready in numbers and physical facilities. I was very shaky at this time. I didn't know what you could do with these kids either. . . . I don't know what the hell was going on. Most of the time I felt very capable. I'd go back and tell somebody how to handle a schizophrenic, this was no problem. Somebody would have a problem about this, I'd go back, I wouldn't know what to do either. This is a difference, I'm sure.

The effects of these experiences were enormous, almost catastrophic, even after the number of adolescents was reduced. The ward staff lost even more confidence in themselves, in the doctors, in the hospital. From December of that year, when the adolescent problem was beginning to be solved by getting rid of them, the staff engaged in a holding operation, some waiting for the future and a permanent medical director to bring better times, some not caring.

No sooner was the adolescent rebellion over than Dr. Dale submitted his resignation as acting director. Dale's announcement of his resignation was a blow to the ward staff which had not been aware of his ambivalence about the directorship. Although he had withdrawn from his former closeness to the ward staff, he was the last of the psychiatrists who symbolized the Crest identity for them. He had been, for the ward staff, the pivotal figure at Crest. It was difficult to conceive of Crest without Dr. Dale.

One aide noted:

> Well, I thought it was very sad [Dale's leaving]. . . . I
> felt that it was a big loss to the hospital and at the same
> time felt that, well, certainly the hospital can't rest on the
> shoulder of one man. But I felt that he was a very strong
> man in the organization, and there was going to be a hole
> that was going to have to be filled by somebody.

Another aide reflected the general uncertainty about Crest which
became critical with Dr. Dale's announcement.

> I was wondering why can't they—if Crest is going along
> fine—why can't they find a doctor that would be suitable
> to take the job? And so I was a little bit suspicious, be-
> cause a year had gone by and they kept saying, well, that
> they were looking for just the right man, and then you
> begin to wonder if they are.

In addition to the aura of failure brought about by the adolescent rebellion and Dr. Dale's resignation, a series of misfortunes
added an aura of death in the hospital. In March, Dr. Morris
Pattman had a coronary. Also in March, Dinah "Molly" Mc-
Carthy—a laundress at the hospital for many years, suddenly
died. Joan Sheehan, a social worker, had to be discharged because
there were not sufficient funds to pay her. Rae Allen, an adolescent ex-patient, who had been discharged from the hospital more
than a month previously, committed suicide in March. In April,
Dr. Pattman was fired. In May, Dr. Dunn, the former director,
no longer in Columbia, died as a result of an accident. It appeared to some to be a suicide. Another adolescent ex-patient,
Milton Averill, died in an accident that had clear suicidal over-
tones. Each of these events had special significance to people at
the hospital. The director of nurses said:

> And I remember with Molly's death, a very peculiar
> thing I felt. Jesus Christ this is really funny, real funny.
> This woman had been healthy as a horse. She was very
> fond of Dunn and I thought well God, the hospital, just
> another one of these things. This was somebody I never
> had to worry about one iota about what went on down
> there. She would fuss a little but that was all. And Miss

> Sheehan's discharge was pretty rough on us because this was the first person that ever had been discharged from Crest for lack of funds. The first person and everyone knew that. . . . Things are really rough when this happens, really rough. I don't think the Allen thing—people really felt sad about this because they were really fond of her. As far as I was concerned I was convinced the hospital was dead, dead, dead, dead. . . . I'll never forget the morning Jim Dale walked in and said did you hear that I had a telephone call last night and George Dunn was dead. Well, I, you know, it was the kind of thing which I thought was crazy, crazy as hell. His influence is still here you know. This is the way I felt. I felt a little creepy about it.

Another nurse spoke about this period:

> Some of this is retrospect and some of it is a very peculiar kind of feeling. The first time I ever had some real funny feelings about Crest was when, let's see, Morris Pattman had his heart attack and then very shortly afterwards Molly died and very shortly thereafter we got this word about George Dunn. And I had the strangest kind of feeling. I remember talking with Ruth Nichols about it one day and we spent a couple of hours just talking about Crest. I had this kind of—well like Harry Stack Sullivan said—I had these feelings of awe or kind of unidentified kinds of feelings about Crest. Like something was very peculiar and I was a little bit scared about being around Crest that I might catch some of this.

One of the early actions of the committee of five consultants was to recommend the discharge of Morris Pattman. The board agreed. The professional staff at the hospital was particularly upset by this action, especially since the firing was announced immediately after Pattman had recovered from a coronary. One of the staff psychiatrists later commented:

> The thing that really angered me in a way that I couldn't do anything about, it was Morris' rather summary dis-

missal. I mean, later on I found out what about: apparently the board got scared, and they called a committee of consultants, asked about finances; and finances particularly related to Morris' salary, which was fairly high. And they simply made a recommendation; and they acted immediately on the recommendation within a matter of a week or so after he had returned to work from a coronary attack. My feeling was I was glad to be out of it. I mean, I spoke to Morris and asked him if there was any way in which I could protest, because it was just so damn god-awful—hell there was nothing I could resign from, I didn't belong to the consulting staff, and who these people were that acted as the hatchet men, I don't know. I meant to just tell the degree of my withdrawal: Morton went out there, remember, spent two days or two half-days a week, and I literally never met him during the months he was there.

The reason given Pattman for his discharge was financial. He received a relatively high salary, but had been producing more income for the hospital through his psychotherapy than had any other psychotherapist. However, with the drop in census, his financial contribution also dropped. Furthermore, Pattman's therapy load was reduced because of the setting up of a rule, through the instigation of the consultants, that the hospital staff were not to treat out-patients. Pattman had been receiving referrals of out-patients for psychotherapy because of his national reputation.

The main group of the consulting staff was not informed of Pattman's discharge until some time later. Some of them reacted unenthusiastically, and even with resentment at the action of their seniors:

> I always felt that . . . this was an absolute disgrace, the firing of him, and I said so. I was at the meeting where the consulting staff—one of these emergency meetings that we had—where a small committee, which by that time had sort of tried to take charge of things . . . announced that Pattman had been fired; and I was abso-

lutely horrified, particularly at the way it was done. It just seemed completely incredible, just completely incredible, that grown-up people could have operated that way.

In May, 1959, Dr. Doren's appointment as the new medical director had been announced. He would not arrive until September. In June of 1959, the hospital professional staff was decimated. Dr. Dale left, as did the two residents. One of the residents, Dr. Rhodes, who had come to Crest in June, 1958, with the plan of remaining as a staff member, was offered a permanent position. He later stated:

> By Christmas time I very strongly felt that I couldn't leave Crest soon enough and the only reason I was staying was because I didn't want to leave in the middle of the year and wanted to get a year's accreditation. I felt under some obligation to stay out my time. But after I had been there three months I just—it was about in there that things began to change. At first, I thought I wanted to work there; and after about four or five months I felt that's the last place in the world I wanted to work. . . . I would say that I've never been exposed or experienced so much anxiety.

Dr. Pattman was in the process of leaving. Thus, in July, 1959, the full-time staff consisted of one psychiatrist, Dr. Preston; a social worker, Miss Simmons; and two psychologists, Drs. Paulson and Post. The latter was in the process of looking for another position, and he left in August. Three full-time professional staff members remained; there had been ten when Dr. Dale assumed the directorship.

After Dale's departure, Dr. Carpenter was appointed as clinical supervisor until the new director arrived. He and Dr. Morton, the acting director, spent only a few hours at the hospital each week. The Public Health Service had refused to continue to support new residents because of the uncertain situation with regard to the directorship of Crest. Although the Crest administration had decided to accept and pay one resident if a good candidate applied, no good ones did. For the first time since 1954 there were no psychiatric residents at Crest. One aide noted:

> I remember feeling some amount of panic when many of the doctors left—do you remember when that was? Rhodes, Rector, and Dale, all cut out at about the same time.

With Drs. Morton and Carpenter at the hospital for so few hours, the day-to-day clinical management of the hospital was accomplished by the only staff psychiatrist, Dr. Preston. He had come to Crest from Menningers several years before as a resident; over this period his reputation had become increasingly good. He was a young, rather calm, yet decisive person. After Dale left, Preston was actually in charge of the hospital until the new director arrived in September.

The consensus among the staff was that Preston did an excellent job in keeping the hospital going that summer. He worked long hours and was able to coordinate the activities of the hospital. His orders to the ward staff were clear, decisive, and helpful. The ward staff did not overburden him with their detailed problems. They felt that since he had so many responsibilities they should not ask him for help unless they really needed it. Yet, when they did apply to him, they felt he responded helpfully and clearly. A relationship of mutual confidence was built up between Preston and the rest of the staff. Preston said:

> I felt quite a good deal of support coming from them. I mean, during this time my word was treated, not as the word of God particularly, but there was a good deal of mutual respect during that summer. . . . I was around a lot; I mean I didn't feel it necessary to take on twenty-five hours of office psychotherapy. I felt that my primary job was the management of patients, and I felt that the management of twenty-two patients was not impossible. And there really, actually, wasn't too much decrease in professional time spent with the staff, since we used morning conferences as conferences instead of just reports, and the formal conferences were reduced but my

feeling at the time was that there was quite a bit of give and take and it was centralized enough so that not nearly as much time was needed. . . . There were a couple of times that I got mad as hell in conference, raised hell with them about what they were doing at the lake and one thing and another. I know some of the people who were a bit closer to me in the ward staff would say, "Well, you know the staff feels you're a bit overloaded," and this and that, but I felt in pretty good touch with the situation. By this time I knew the people pretty well. I don't think during the summer that I knew the new people as well as I had known the new people when I was a resident, but I felt that I was in pretty good contact with the key people.

Some staff members noted:

It seemed to me like it was a very good period. I personally regarded Preston very highly in his judgment and treatment of patients. I mean, I felt that he really, he knew what he was doing, and if he didn't know what he was doing, he didn't make you feel that he didn't know. And I admired that quality alone because I know how important it is for everybody to feel that a doctor knows how he wants things done, and he certainly had this ability. I think, more than that, he really did have good judgment in his treatment of patients.

During the Preston period I think things went very well. I don't think I was very interested, but everything as far as orders and staff—everything just suddenly settled down. . . . Preston came over in the evening, he lived five minutes from the hospital; they felt very free to call him; and my own personal feeling is that he did a tremendous job—frankly, very tremendous job.

Preston's administration was a temporary one; he was to be replaced shortly by a permanent director. Morale was better; the staff was marking time, its hopes pinned on the new director.

The new director was viewed as someone who might solve all the hospital's problems.

> This was the period when everybody says there was going to be a new medical director; and things picked up then, because people were excited that we were going to have a new medical director; and he was going to be the salvation, you know.

CHAPTER SEVEN

An Epidemic of Suicide in a Dying Hospital

> The [board] president welcomed Dr. Thomas Doren, the new medical director, and asked for any "first impressions" comments the latter might have to make. In brief, Dr. Doren emphasized that the fundamental question regarding Crest is its existence in terms of the financial problems. On the whole he is inclined to an optimistic attitude particularly in view of the continued high morale of the staff maintained under difficult circumstances. He believes that Crest's basic program and service is good, but feels that the question is can we afford this "custom" treatment? If not, should we change our type of service and in what way.

The last year of Crest's existence was marked by a series of crises which engaged all who were involved with the hospital. Although everyone shared in the general anxiety about the hospital which characterized this period, strikingly, each of the different groups—the board, the consulting staff, and the hospital staff— focused on different sources of concern. The board saw itself as pressed by a massive financial need which threatened the very

160

existence of Crest. Because of the financial problem, it called in the consulting staff for support. The consultants, then, once again, became actively involved with the hospital. Starting from the financial need, they regarded Crest as obsolete, and concerned themselves with changes in the hospital's structure, theoretical orientation, and treatment philosophy. At the same time, the crises facing the staff at the hospital centered around the deterioration of the old identity of Crest, the lack of an adequate substitute identity, and the consequent ineffectiveness of clinical functioning. The board and the consulting staff were scarcely aware of the full extent of the decline in treatment effectiveness and in staff morale at the hospital. Meanwhile, at the hospital, the money problem was given little credence. Each group was concerned with its own immediate problems, and all felt that Crest's existence was at stake.

The one individual involved with all of the problems was the medical director. In a "Report on Observations, Opinions and Recommendations Regarding Crest Foundation Hospital, Based on My First Four Months as Medical Director," dated January 28, 1960, the director eloquently described the situation on his arrival:

> I began my duties as Medical Director on September 16, 1959. On that date the census was at a low level, namely 19 patients, and the staff was in all areas reduced to the minimal effective number, only one psychiatrist, besides myself, one social worker, and one psychologist. The nursing and aide staff was more nearly at its normal level, but the Director of Nurses was just beginning an extended leave to pursue her educational plans. This composition of staff was in marked contrast to the situation at the height of Crest's previous functioning, when there were five psychiatrists, two social workers and three psychologists. (THE PROFESSIONAL STAFF TOTAL ON SEPTEMBER 16, 1959 WAS FOUR. EIGHT MONTHS EARLIER THE NUMBER WAS ELEVEN.)
>
> The hospital was operating at a deficit of at least $3000 to $4000 per month and the deficit was being covered by

mortgages on the property. THE FUNDS COVERING THIS DEFICIT WILL BE DEPLETED IN APRIL 1960. The buildings and grounds, though in fair condition, generally were sorely in need of repair in many areas; additions and replacements were also necessary. There was a partially finished new building, in no way usable. Funds were not available for its completion. Furniture in most of the patients rooms needed replacement. The facilities in general were minimally adequate. There was no semblance of the ideal model hospital design or structure. For example, the North Wing, which is used for the most disturbed patients and for maximum security, had windows which could be, and often were, broken by patients. There was no area where a noisy patient could be kept without disturbing all the other patients and the staff in that section. The result was that when one patient would become unusually noisy and disturbed, all of the other patients would be affected similarly.

The training program had become nearly defunct. The Public Health stipends for residents had been discontinued as of July 1, 1959 because there was not a full-time Medical Director.

The research project which had been under way for over a year on a Public Health grant was not working out as expected. Though considerable data had been accumulated, its value was limited on the basis of its not fulfilling the expectations and the premises of the project.

The miracle was: Under these very adverse conditions the hospital was functioning as well as it was. This was due largely to the excellent core of staff that remained. Their morale was good, but shaky.

The Board had interest but seemed to be somewhat confused in direction and purpose, from the standpoint of providing much-needed monies. The confusion of the Board members where it existed was largely due, I believe, to confused hospital leadership in the past. Their primary project of obtaining a medical director had, however, been achieved.

The consulting staff was also an interested group but was not sure just what its purpose and function was. An Advisory Committee of the Consulting Staff had been most effective and interested in evaluating some of the basic problems, and in recruiting a new Medical Director. However, this function was literally in the hands of a few people on the Committee. The Consulting Staff was as a whole relatively inactive.

It appeared to me that both the Consulting Staff and the Board, perhaps the hospital staff as well, had been operating to some degree on the basis of an illusion. This illusion was essentially that Crest was an ideal psychiatric institution—that by being such it would maintain itself. Although this may be stated in the extreme, I intended it to point out the deficiencies in the realistic appraisal of the situation, which was, namely, Crest was operating well in service to patients, and though the philosophy of treatment was ideal, the conditions and circumstances of the operation were far from ideal. Constantly there was the reference to the fact that it is not the buildings and grounds, etc., which are important, but rather it is the treatment philosophy. Though this is basically true, to my mind this does not excuse by any means the poor condition of the facilities. The situation reminded me somewhat of an aloof Southern family struggling to maintain the ante-bellum aristocracy, in spite of reality being blatantly to the contrary.

Regarding the patients at Crest, my impressions are borne out by other professional people with more experience at this hospital than I have yet had. At the beginning of the hospital's existence the patient load was more typically like that of the general psychiatric hospital. The proportion of difficult treatment cases has definitely increased. The corollary is that the proportion of the more rapid treatment cases has continually decreased. There are various reasons for this. One is that Crest has come to be thought of as a place where patients go to stay a long time. Another is that Crest is much more expensive than other psychiatric hospitals, and a third, that the number of psychiatrists in Columbia has practically doubled in the last five years and tripled in the last ten. This means a larger number of the younger psychiatrists, especially take their patients to other psychiatric hospitals where they are able to treat them more directly. At Crest the patients are essentially turned over to the hospital staff for their treatment and management in the hospital, though they might be taken to doctor's offices downtown for treatment interviews if their condition permits.

A word about the census. It is true that the census of the hospital is of vital importance in determining the cost of operations, particularly the amount of the deficit. However, to put off providing any of the basic needs until the census stabilizes at a high number is not realistic. The number of census will depend vitally in various ways upon the provision of the outlined needs.

This then was the picture when I arrived, and it was in truth much worse than I had expected to find it. To my knowledge the hospital has never been on a solid basis in terms of its leadership nor its financial structure. Further, at the time of my arrival it was at its lowest ebb in most respects. Its outstanding assets were the people, the staff, and also the Board's interest and, I hope, potential effectiveness. When I stepped into this position I readily learned that the Board and staff had another illusion, namely that the mere fact of my arrival would solve the problems magically.

Dr. Doren's description was valid. And it was certainly true that he was counted upon to save the institution. During the summer preceding Doren's arrival, the belief was constantly expressed at the hospital that a new director could save Crest; all hope for the restoration of the hospital to its previous high level of functioning was centered on the new director. As soon as Dr. Doren's appointment was announced, the hopes of the hospital staff rose. Some ward staff members recalled:

And then Doren came, and he was the hope of everyone; he was the medical director that was going to steady Crest, make Crest pull together . . . everyone thought it was going to be great. . . . I think everyone welcomed Dr. Doren with open arms.

I felt that, you know, well, we got a medical director, maybe we'll get some residents and things will begin to look better.

I was glad there was going to be a permanent medical director. I felt this was a step forward, things would look up now.

Doren made an excellent early impression on the professional staff. Dr. Preston stated: "He was an enthusiastic participant in treatment. . . . Fine, you know, let's try a new way, wonderful; the old ways are tiresome and unrewarding and tough." Dr. Paulson was pleased with Dr. Doren's optimism, one example of which lay in Dr. Doren's view that patients could do with shorter periods of hospitalization than had become the norm for Crest.

The staff also saw him as a man capable of dealing with the community in carrying out the necessary public relations functions of the director of Crest.

I did admire him. . . . Here was a guy who was starting to do something for Crest on the outside. Also, here was the guy who—well, he wasn't a businessman but he could—he was that type of person who could socialize with people on the outside and really be tactful.

For a while there seemed to be more enthusiasm, because he got out and started working in the community and getting people interested in Crest, or trying anyway, and I think that he was really trying.

I think that most everyone was real optimistic, that the guy seemed to be a real ball of fire, seemed to be well-qualified, to be very likeable; and I think the general attitude was probably better. I think things were being done, you see things happening. . . .

Morale rose. The staff felt that Dr. Doren would fulfill their hopes and desires, that the deteriorating identity of Crest would be strengthened and reaffirmed.

The staff's high hopes soon were drowned in disappointment. Dr. Doren did not reaffirm the Crest identity. Rather, he functioned to change it, by attempting to offer a new "way" to Crest. Needless to say, the change itself was disturbing to some Crestites. In addition, Doren was not an inspiring leader; and the new identity he offered—and there were many who were ready to accept any clear way—was not particularly exciting or creative. The therapeutic philosophy Dr. Doren offered Crest was an eclectic one. Stressing flexibility and reasonableness, where Crest had rigidly adhered to psychological treatment, Dr. Doren believed that the total psychiatric therapeutic armamentarium should be available. Thus, he took the position that drugs and shock treatment, if felt to be "indicated to further the patient's comfort and recovery," should be used, although only "adjunctively" to psychotherapy, which was the genuine and significant treatment. His views, it should be noted, were not unlike those of many of Crest's critics among the consultants.

The imposition of Dr. Doren's way of thinking affected morale in the hospital. The old Crest identity was not only not reaffirmed, but was undermined in many crucial ways. Most important, many of the staff felt that Dr. Doren had taken over all responsibility, and did not give others the independence of function and respect they had previously enjoyed. The ward staff felt that Dr. Doren placed little value on their significance in the treatment process. The other professional personnel, and even the hospital administrator, considered that their roles had been undercut.

As has been made clear, milieu therapy and the ward staff's function within this approach were crucial aspects of the Crest identity. The ward staff were held in high esteem and their significance always affirmed. Dr. Doren, it was believed, thought differently about the usefulness of the ward staff in the treatment process. He was perceived as considerably more authoritarian in relation to the ward staff, and acute resentment developed. Some nurses and aides commented:

When he first came here, you know, he was so critical of the aide staff and these intellectual creeps running around . . . simple kindly people could take as good care of the patients as some of these people that are so preoccupied with dynamics, and so on.

I felt that Dr. Doren never gave dignity to the jobs of the people in the hospital, that he didn't have regard for other people's ability to work well, that he didn't give people an opportunity to really talk to him. He let them talk, but he wasn't moved by it, and I felt there were a lot of people who worked out there who were very capable of telling him a few things. Now I don't mean that in a smart kind of way. I felt that any time you have a group of trained people they've learned some things that they can tell him, because they're with the patient in different circumstances than he is; and I felt that it was a mistake for him to take over so much of the management of patients. I thought if he was going to be a therapist he should be a therapist and let the management go to another doctor.

One thing I always felt with Doren . . . that the staff wasn't needed really as much as before, or, you didn't need as highly a skilled staff as before.

I had the feeling that he had even less regard for ward staff . . . than anybody ever had.

Another important difficulty of the ward staff which had complex repercussions was a consequence of Doren's participation in the hospital treatment of all patients. This was another change; always before, one person, the managing physician, was responsible for the patient's hospital treatment. Moreover, Doren's activity with all patients raised questions about the relationship between the two psychiatrists in the hospital.

Dr. Doren made it known quite clearly that he was medical director and that he . . . could change any order given by any doctor without discussion.

I felt a good deal of disagreement between the two of

them. [I got orders from] both, which was quite a switch, really, and sometimes specific . . . contradicted one another.

Dr. Doren started to write orders on all these patients, which we resented very much; not so much that he wrote the orders, but the fact that he would not discuss them as we always did. And of course we were in such a rut up there, where only the managing doctor wrote orders, you know, and we had asked Dr. Preston about this. Say he wrote orders on a patient, well, what the hell is the scoop here? And finally, . . . here it was really brought out, the fact that something was rotten in Denmark between Preston and Doren; and finally I remember it came out that we brought this up in nurses' class.

Well, another aide and I . . . were confused about this, and I sort of wanted to know right now who is her managing doctor. We were so hot and bothered about it, I don't remember why now, but we wanted to talk to both doctors; what was the scoop, who was the boss here? . . . at this point, we were both real hot-blooded on this issue and would put in calls that we wanted to talk to both of them right now. About this time, Dr. Preston showed up on the ward and we said to him: just what's the scoop, tell us what's going on, who's the managing doctor? And maybe he said that he was, but what he added was: you know, he's my boss too—and this really shook me. I thought: well for heaven's sake, what's going on here? I had never come across this openly before and I'm sure you know there were dozens of times when the nursing staff—the aide staff—or me in particular, when we did or didn't get scuttlebutt . . . and I'm sure lots of times it was very smoothly covered up so that the staff wasn't supposed to know about it and all that business. But to have Dr. Preston say point-blank that—well, it seemed to me he was saying that he really had no say-so, whatever Dr. Doren said, went. This particular point bothered me. And for some reason or other, we [aides] . . . asked to talk to him [Doren] about it; but somehow I didn't really care anymore.

The nursing staff's perception of difficulties between members of the upper level of the hierarchy, the professionals, was accurate. The problems were intense and took a number of forms. Everyone found it difficult to communicate adequately with Dr. Doren. The nonmedical members of the professional staff felt that his orientation was emphatically medical—"a big medical man"—and that he did not respect their professional disciplines. The result was a taste of bitterness in the relationships between professional staff members. However, this did not affect the hospital as a whole as greatly as did the conflict between Dr. Doren and Dr. Preston, the two psychiatrists.

The conflict between the psychiatrists took two forms. First, Doren as medical director participated in the treatment of all the patients in the hospital, and wrote orders on many. This meant that he wrote orders on Dr. Preston's patients, which, as noted above, was uncommon at Crest. Second, the two psychiatrists thought differently about the hospital management of acutely disturbed patients. Their orders to the staff, then, would often be radically different in similar situations. This was confusing to the ward staff; it became an acute problem when the two men were writing orders on the same patient.

Doren stated that his participation with Preston's patients was very limited, and that he had had no intention of interfering with Preston's treatment of patients. He observed that he might have written some orders "while I was covering on a week-end when something would come up." He added, "What there was in my intent and my participation . . . to my mind there was no need for this to be a problem. The readiness of the staff to see it as one, kind of surprised me." He noted that Preston "did make a comment or two" about his feeling that he [Doren] was

> . . . interfering or that I was putting him in a compromised position, which was certainly not my intention. . . . I don't know how much of it was on the basis of Preston's own feelings about me in a competitive sense. . . . But the thing that was most confusing to me

in the discussion of all these things later, was that if these things existed why was there such a strong feeling of reflecting what I felt might be possessiveness on the one hand, or assumption that there would be a conflict on the other hand? And if these things did exist, why did they have to be dealt with malignantly?

Dr. Preston's view was different. "Doren just didn't think like the staff was used to having a physician think," and this

> . . . had to do with drugs and the shock, and most importantly, delegation. It wasn't customary until Doren's coming for one physician to have anything to do with another physician's patients. . . . Doren's approach was tremendously manipulative. He didn't just supervise, he acted. . . . He had all kinds of ideas . . . but he didn't just have ideas, he moved. And I wasn't used to this. . . . It took me a hell of a while to come around to the point of saying to him, you must leave my patients alone; because when he meddled it was always with such good intentions. And I must say I submerged; I didn't get angry with him.

Preston commented on an experience with one patient:

> I got out of it as quickly as I could. I mean, I still continued occasionally to write the orders and was kind of in the position of a message-carrier for a while, where I would be writing orders on this guy, but Doren would be telling. I mostly withdrew . . . I got out.

Perhaps at least as crucial as this issue was the difference in the treatment techniques of the two men, which was more apparent in therapeutic action than in theoretical discussion. The difference was highlighted when the physicians were called on to respond to a request from an anxious patient, a not uncommon situation in the hospital. Preston characteristically would say no to the request until the patient could show him that it was reasonable. Doren characteristically would say yes to the request, unless it was obviously and apparently unreasonable. Thus, patients on the same ward, or, at times, the same patient, would be treated in very different ways.

The conflict between the psychiatrists had repercussions among the ward staff. Miss Nelson, the new director of nurses, was caught in the middle. She had taken the place, temporarily, of Ruth Nichols. She had been put in an uncomfortable position at best, and was, as one aide put it: "handed the hottest potato in history." Miss Nichols had left in October, supposedly for six months of work at school; not until February did it become clear that she was not going to come back. Miss Nelson sided with Dr. Preston's approach to patient treatment. They had developed professionally together at Crest and they joined together in the "Crest way." The difference between the psychiatrists' approach to patients was important, since Miss Nelson had to defend and support the physician's therapeutic actions and plans in her discussions with the staff. That is, when orders were given, if the staff had questions, they came through Miss Nelson, who had to attempt to get the orders carried out.

Miss Nelson was very unhappy with Dr. Doren. She felt in her relationship with him a "constant whittling away at one's self-confidence." Yet, she had her job to do. One aide told of a situation where Miss Nelson "called a number of us together, and wanted to know just what was going on in the closed ward."

> The deal was that really we weren't giving Dr. Doren a chance, that we just shut him out, and the kids found it difficult to communicate with him. Well, Joan pointed out to us that since the very moment Dr. Doren had gotten there, that we had demanded action from him, we wanted answers, and wanted answers that would solve problems, and we wanted him to produce right now, and we had never given him a chance to sort of get into the swing. She pointed out that whereas Dr. Dale used to be able to sit and listen to anxious people just yammer at him and demand action responses, he could take it, and eventually offer some calm honest good advice. Dr. Doren couldn't take this, and we were just pushing him to a degree that he had to stay away from us; he had to

> stay away from the closed ward even. And she wanted to know what we all thought. . . . I don't know how the other people involved left the meeting, but I left the meeting thinking I must do everything I can to support Dr. Doren and give him a chance. . . .

The fact was that all too often Miss Nelson found herself in a position of supporting a treatment program with which she didn't agree. And, together with all the other professional people, she was handicapped by the difficulty in communicating with Dr. Doren.

The most impossible situation occurred for Miss Nelson after a time when Doren had "interfered in a way which annoyed Preston."

> [Preston] said you tell your nurses that they are not to ask Doren for any orders at all [on my patients] except for emergencies. And I did it. . . . I was mad at him too. And I made a mistake. I should have said to Preston: "now look, this is your responsibility. You tell Doren what you don't want him to do. Don't put this on me." But I didn't, and I made a mistake. I was in the middle, and I was getting squeezed.

Thus, in the first few months of Dr. Doren's directorship, confusion, conflict, and anxiety characterized the atmosphere of the hospital. As director, as the senior and ultimately responsible person, Dr. Doren acted with the patients and the staff according to his own theoretical orientation. As has been illustrated, this approach differed from that which had developed at Crest, and which had identified Crest. With the old identity dead, and anxiety rampant, many of the staff members were searching for, and prepared to accept, a new identity. A crisis in the staff's evaluation of Dr. Doren's approach occurred in the case of Mr. Joseph Ullman, who was given electric convulsive (shock) treatment. Two of the most influential staff members were preparing themselves, though in a somewhat resigned fashion, to accept even this dramatic change from the old Crest identity. Miss Nelson reported:

I had said to myself that I would have to accept the idea of shock treatment. I felt sure Doren was oriented this way, that I would have to change.

Dr. Preston stated:

Well, part of shock treatment too had do to with we've got to become a different kind of hospital. We can no longer be a . . . hospital where organic treatments are not used. . . . [we have to change as] part of getting more patients, increasing our census. . . . We've got to change our approach—I mean this was something that Doren was saying.

Mr. Joseph Ullman, a man in his early thirties, was admitted to Crest in early December, 1959. He was seen as an intensely suicidal individual. The use of ECT in cases of this sort might in many institutions be considered routine; but at Crest it was a rather dramatic occurrence. Crest's philosophy was "psychological treatment for the psychologically ill." From time to time, with particularly difficult patients, tranquilizing drugs had been used—with more frequency since Dr. Doren's regime—but always somewhat ambivalently. Shock had not been used since October, 1957, when it was given to a woman over sixty, who had received more than a year's treatment with no noticeable progress. She was given one ECT, and died shortly afterward. ECT had been used rarely if at all in the two years prior to 1957. The use of shock for a man of Ullman's age and intellectual capacity was strikingly inconsistent with the staff's beliefs. But the Ullman case illustrates in many ways the state of affairs at the hospital in early December. It is noteworthy that although Mr. Ullman was seen as a determinedly suicidal person, there is much reason, in retrospect, to question whether this diagnostic appraisal was correct.[1]

The conference held on Ullman, where the use of shock was decided upon, was one in which the overriding attitude was one

[1] See the detailed description of the Ullman case in Arthur L. Kobler and Ezra Stotland, *The End of Hope: A Social-Clinical Study of Suicide* (New York: Free Press of Glencoe, 1964).

of helplessness. In retrospect, it is striking to note that helplessness of such an extreme sort had set in in such a short time, less than a week after Ullman's admission. One staff member stated:

> We had a conference, a staff administrative conference on Tuesday morning, devoted to Ullman; and at that conference the feeling was expressed that we were helpless in dealing with this man. He was forcing us to treat him in such a regressed way—that is, to facilitate his regression—that we had a choice of either regressing him all the way or doing something to break up this pattern. It was a feeling of helplessness; and the expression was repeated that he had us over a barrel. And it was at that time that ECT was raised and agreed on by most everybody, including I even think myself—although begrudgingly—but then, I wasn't in touch with the thing. But I think everybody agreed, in frustration.

A factor which cannot be overlooked in this case was the pressure from the relatives, since there is question whether in the hospital's vulnerable state the relatives did not significantly influence the treatment. Dr. Doren spoke of the patient's father and uncle telephoning, "pressuring us into giving electroshock." This occurred "almost from the beginning."

> This was pressure, but I am quite certain in my own mind that this had very little to do, if anything, with our deciding to give it. This is one of the reasons why it was presented to the whole staff for consideration and decision—to minimize the factor of the family—because Dr. Preston was the one getting the family pressure. I got some of it myself, but he was the one getting most of it.

Dr. Preston's view is somewhat different. After agreeing that the staff felt helpless, he added:

> We were in a box. The important relatives were just saying by God the only way to treat this guy was with ECT and it's malpractice if you don't, because the ECT will help him. And Doren was strongly considering ECT.

> . . . And I wasn't concerned terribly that this guy was going to kill himself, but I felt like I'd be in a hell of a spot if he did anything to himself and I hadn't given him ECT.

Some of the nursing staff felt electroshock was used primarily not because of the needs of the patient but rather because of the needs of the staff. One aide, in explaining her view of the difficulty in the treatment with Ullman, said:

> No communication between the doctor and the individual that was working with the patient and was assigned to the patient all the time, and that was me. And speaking of him, it is a very peculiar thing that I, of all people on the closed section, should have been assigned to Mr. Ullman, because I disagreed with his treatment from the very beginning. His treatment—electric shock treatment. To me, Mr. Ullman's electric shock treatment was not for Mr. Ullman; it was for certain ward staff, or doctors, or whoever. It was for their anxiety. We were treating anxiety but not the patient. That's the way I felt about it.

The staff was divided about the issue of shock. A head nurse stated that her personnel "were very much against it." The director of nurses said: "Most of us felt that if shock were ever indicated, that this probably was the time." In subsequent individual interviews, the nurses and aides who worked with Ullman presented varied points of view, some feeling that it was the thing to do, others strongly opposed to it. In the light of the history and philosophy of Crest, ECT could be used at best ambivalently; for some, feeling helpless, the need for a new way was compelling. A head nurse on the closed section stated:

> We as personnel on the ward can only go so far and then you have to use a gimmick to help us, whether it be tranquilizers, sub-coma insulin or ECT. . . . If it helps the staff it helps the patient. I think everything is so closely connected that you can't just separate it.

The conflict within the professional staff, and the ambiguity of the doctors' roles in this case also appear significant. Dr. Preston was the patient's managing physician, and later, on the day of the last shock treatment, he was assigned as the patient's therapist. Yet he did not give the ECT; Dr. Doren did. For although Dr. Preston had more than six years of active hospital experience he had never given an ECT. Moreover, Dr. Preston was as strong a proponent as any person on the staff for "psychological treatment for the psychologically disturbed."

In relation to the pressure by the relatives in this case, Dr. Doren said that Dr. Preston was getting most of the pressure. Dr. Preston stated, contrariwise:

> There had been really no position taken by Doren. You know, the way we treat patients here like this is without ECT, and if you don't like it you can go climb a tree, but if you want it here, this is the way we treat them. This is the way you have to deal with these issues.

This attitude was characteristic of Dr. Preston's method of handling pressure by relatives. He tended to make it clear that he was in control of the treatment; the relatives could take it or leave it. In this case, although he was nominally responsible for the patient, the responsibility was in good part assumed by Dr. Doren. Dr. Preston was aware of this and found his position quite vague. A nurse stated:

> I thought Dr. Preston's responsibility for the patient was usurped by Dr. Doren, that the responsibility for the patient's management clearly was taken by Dr. Doren, and that he was the one who made the decision about the shock, for instance. Dr. Preston had said to me personally that he was not in sympathy with this.

A head nurse stated that she felt that Dr. Preston did not know "exactly what to do as far as management of the patient was concerned. In this particular instance with Ullman what we needed was a strong figure." She added, "There was a big difference of opinion in the management, I am sure, between Dr. Preston and Dr. Doren . . . for instance, the example of ECT.

Dr. Doren wanted to give ECT pretty definitely, but he had to buck Crest to do it."

Mr. Ullman was given three shock treatments. Since he appeared to be markedly improved, and "available" for psychotherapy, the course of ECT was stopped. Ten days later, Mr. Ullman's glasses, which had remained a subject of great controversy since Mr. Ullman was still regarded as a suicidal risk, were left in his night stand. They were found the following morning amidst much fearful comment. Two hours later, Mr. Ullman made a suicide attempt, cutting his throat and wrists with his broken glasses. Mr. Ullman's suicide attempt clearly destroyed for the staff Dr. Doren's "new identity" for Crest. Moreover, Mr. Ullman's suicide attempt was the prologue for an epidemic of suicides—three suicides in three weeks—by far the most destructive blow to the hospital staff's confidence and morale. Although it is not possible or necessary to describe this epidemic in great detail here, certain facts are pertinent.[2]

Mr. Ullman was taken to a general hospital, and returned a day later, his wounds sutured. It was soon decided that he could not be treated at Crest and plans were made to transfer him. Anxiety about suicide pervaded the hospital.

The staff reactions to Ullman's suicide attempt were extreme. A nurse stated:

> At any rate, the patient did make this very serious suicidal attempt—and you know the reaction to that was something really quite fantastic. The patient did not die. The thing was handled. It was obvious from the beginning that he was not going to die, because he didn't cut any vessels which could exsanguinate him; and yet the anxiety around this man was just fantastic. It was as though the guy had really killed himself. (Anxiety on whose part?) On Dr. Doren's, Dr. Preston's, the ward staff, everybody, and it was absurd, and something with which I couldn't empathize, and didn't understand. From

[2] See Kobler and Stotland, *The End of Hope.*

that time on, I think there was no decrease of anxiety on the closed section.

The head nurse on Ullman's ward said:

> Of course, the thing that bothered me also on suicidals—which I think in a way hinges on this problem—is what do you do with a guy once he has tried to commit suicide, and you keep him in a hospital? I'll speak staff-wise, for the personnel on the ward. Nobody wanted to work with him. They were afraid. And this had actually been said: "What if something happens to him while I'm working with him? I don't want that responsibility." This is what it amounted to. So as a charge nurse making out assignments it was very difficult to get anybody to work with him, because they felt they had to watch him continuously after he had attempted and almost made it. So he couldn't move. Even if he was able to move, we wouldn't let him move. We wouldn't let the doctor let him move. The safest place for him was in bed with restraints on. And I went to the other extreme. If he went up to take a bath, I insisted myself to go, because I didn't want anyone else to take the responsibility. I was charge nurse; this was my responsibility; I had to take it.

The nurse went on to say that after the attempt the staff became "much more cautious."

> We've had other patients who have tried stuff, things in their mouth or around their neck, and it never seemed to bother too many people. . . . But after the attempt was made and almost succeeded, this is where the staff freezes up and nobody wants to take a chance on him then. And even the managing doctor didn't want to take a chance.

Another staff member said:

> If there is such a thing possible as the idea of suicide impregnating the air and the climate and the atmosphere being highly charged with it, this was certainly true.

> How much patients might have felt this, that had been communicated to them, and had homicidal or suicidal tendencies stimulated merely by this . . . I think this is quite possible because everyone was on their toes. They were watching. When you would be in the closed section office any unusual noise, people would jump. When we would hear the telephone ring at lunch, everyone would tense up.

This intense anxiety about suicide was in striking contrast to the attitude toward suicide at Crest in the past. Crest in its nine years of existence had experienced one suicide, in May, 1954; and very few patients had made severe suicidal attempts while at the hospital. Previous to the epidemic, the attitude of the staff—the nursing staff as well as the professional staff—had been one of confidence. This attitude was not a casual one; on the contrary, it was in their view a cautious one. But they did not expect suicide, and they felt that they could control the danger. This set of attitudes was almost unanimous. One nurse, high in the hierarchy, reports that when she joined the staff she was told there had been only one abortive suicide attempt.

> This was the only suicide attempt they had. And they were pretty pleased about this and this was one of the things I remember their telling of, that this was the only suicide attempt they had. And we had no suicide attempts in the early days of this thing that I can remember.

When asked whether there was any problem or preoccupation with the problem of suicide in his memory, an aide said:

> No, I don't think there was. I can't remember. Well, if we knew someone was on S precautions we'd check them, but we were self-confident that they wouldn't commit, because we weren't concerned about it—because we were in control of the situation. I think that is a different feeling than what was later. I can remember that I wasn't concerned about somebody who was going to kill them-

selves. I never thought they would because I was not going to let them. I mean, I felt in control. And I think this was a general feeling.

Other statements run in the same vein. "I think the staff was very confident and diligent." "On the locked ward we had control. . . . On the wards I don't think anybody particularly worried that they could put it over on us. Either on the grounds, or off-grounds, maybe they could do it, but not when they were on the wards." Referring to the chief nurse, an aide observed: "She was a very shrewd psychiatric nurse who never never let it slip, never let anybody become lulled into the feeling that suicide in the hospital was impossible just because the hospital happened to be Crest."

A recreational therapist added:

> Patients were sometimes put on suicide precautions; and I think that everybody was certainly cognizant of the patients who were considered very suicidal. But I don't think it was ever a real problem. I mean, I didn't have the feeling the people twitted about it. They knew it, and if—for instance, I used to at that time take patients to movies once a week; and if there was a patient who was considered suicidal, I certainly was aware of it, and I did things I felt were necessary. That is, I never permitted patients to go to the bathroom alone if we were at the movies or anything of this sort. If they were suicidal, I would be sure to put them in the middle in driving to town, and this kind of thing. But it didn't upset me. I felt like I had the situation in hand and it was covered. . . . I would take a male aide with me and I would sit at one end of the row and he would sit at the other, and then we would know when anybody left and automatically he would go with men and I would go with the women, and we would let each other know that we were leaving for that short time.

The professional staff's views were similar. One psychiatrist stated:

I never felt it was a particular problem. I always trusted the nursing staff. I felt that they were very careful. I felt that we had adequate restraints. I felt that the closed section was a pretty darn safe place, and I felt that if some people—if they are going to kill themselves under those circumstances, there just wasn't much you could do about it. And taking that attitude I figured we would do everything we could within reason imposed by the physical plant, and that was all we could do. . . .

A psychiatric resident, when asked about concern about suicide during the period he was at Crest, said:

Well, there weren't any. The question that comes to my mind is how much did we think about it. I don't think we thought about it very much. . . . I think, looking at this in hindsight, as just somebody somewhere, probably the nursing staff, anticipated this kind of thing and set up pretty good rules. There was, as I saw, a rather conservative attitude, that when patients were sick they stayed put on the ward. . . . And in trying to evaluate the ward function at that time in that respect, I would say it was pretty optimistic atmosphere. It was sort of an atmosphere that, no matter what happens we ought to figure out something to do about it, which I think was conveyed to the patient, not in a sense of franticness . . . in a conservative optimism.

Following Mr. Ullman's suicide attempt, on December 23, 1959, the atmosphere of the hospital was redolent of anything but confidence. The old Crest identity was gone; the new identity had failed. The hopes for an inspiring leader had disappeared; and strong leadership was not available. The anxiety of the total staff, provoked by the continuing contact with a noticeably patched-up Mr. Ullman, centered around the danger of suicide. It was in this context that the epidemic of suicides occurred.

On January 1, Mr. Harry Einston, a man in his early twenties, who was out on a pass for New Year's Eve did not return. He was found dead a few days later in his car, in a lonely country spot.

On January 16, Mr. William Oakson, a man in his early sixties, who had been discharged nine days before, and who was due at the hospital for a therapy interview, killed himself.

On January 19, Mrs. Virginia Arlington strangled herself in her room on the closed ward of the hospital while on suicide precautions.

Some of the comments of the staff people about the individuals who killed themselves illustrate the feeling and atmosphere in the hospital during this time. About Mr. Einston, Dr. Doren noted:

> Einston seemed to be going along. He had had several passes, and had his car, and various things seemed to be going all right until . . . the time after Ullman's suicidal attempt. I think the whole air and the atmosphere was charged with anxiety in the whole hospital. There is no doubt of this. I think that this was particularly so with Preston after that situation with Ullman. . . . But I think that Preston pulled back and lost some of his sensitivity to Einston's situation . . . not directly between Einston and Ullman as much as Ullman affecting the staff, particularly Preston, and that affecting Einston. I think this is the important relationship. Well, with Einston's suicide, this heightened the anxiety more. I think everybody reacted with a tightening up. Everybody was scared. Everybody was concerned.

Dr. Preston stated:

> When I found he wasn't returned, I had an immediate fantasy that he suicided; and I suppose this is a summation of the other side of the coin that came to my mind, and it was not unstimulated by things that had gone on previously, but nonetheless, this is my first fantasy. I wonder really where this guy is. And, he's perfectly capable of worrying us in this kind of thing. And he wasn't just worrying us—he's dead.

About Mr. Oakson, the second suicide, Dr. Doren, who was his therapist, said:

> As far as this in relation to others: I think that probably the possibility is that perhaps I had withdrawn somewhat libidinously myself in reaction to Ullman's attempt. Einston's success in suicide, and being particularly concerned with the whole position of the hospital in this and my position in the community. Regardless of whose patient it was, it was my patient that did this, did commit suicide, at least I would be identified as the . . . well, in these other things, Oakson was pretty much out of the picture during all these incidents. He came back somewhere in this thing, and I know when he came back I was hoping he wouldn't find out about these, which is a reflection, I think, of maybe my withdrawing, of maybe anxiety, maybe a little more wish to keep him away because it would be bad for him if he were to know about the suicides, I felt, and I think this was true.

The ward staff reaction to Mrs. Arlington's suicide can be illustrated by a report from the nurses' notes concerning another patient:

> Mr. Elting was upset by the procedures when patient Arlington was removed from the ward. This involved locking his door twice, all the patients were locked in their rooms at these times, that is, when the coroner came in and when she was removed. As I unlocked the door the first time, he peered down the hall and asked what was going on; who had entered the ward, and so forth, was everyone's door locked? I explained that this was so and that everything was under control. Attempted to pressure me for details. When door was locked the second time, he became quite paranoid (sic) and unable to accept my explanation that patient Arlington had been transferred. As I explained this to him, he pressured for more details and asked, "Are you sure? You're looking at me in a very funny way." Was convinced that whatever was happening concerned him. When told this had nothing to do

with him, he either demanded reassurance or said that I was lying to him.

The group of suicides, coming on the heels of conflict, hopelessness, leaderlessness, and helplessness was the crowning blow to the morale of the ward staff. Anxiety prevailed throughout the hospital. No formal attempt was made to deal with the anxiety, nor was there any formal discussion of the suicides. They were discussed informally—in whispers. Not until May did the professional staff meet for the special purpose of discussing the group of suicides, and of considering the hospital's responsibility for them.

Discussion of the suicides was similarly limited outside the hospital. The executive committee of the board was told about the suicides, and there were some peripheral references at a regular board meeting; but most of the members of the board were not aware of the number of suicides that had taken place until late summer of 1960, six or seven months after their occurrence. While a note about the suicide of Mr. Einston was delivered to the consulting staff on January 14, the president and vice president of the consulting staff had no knowledge of the number of suicides which had occurred.

Nor had the epidemic come to an end. In June, yet another patient, while on suicide precautions, escaped and killed herself. One other suicide, which affected the staff, but which is not considered part of this epidemic, occurred in May. A patient who had been discharged a month before, but who was still seeing one of the consultants for treatment, shot herself, succumbing from the wound a month later.

This, then, was the clinical crisis which was the focus at the hospital. The board was concerned with a financial crisis, and, like the hospital staff, they looked to new director Doren for salvation. Some of the board members commented:

> We referred to Doren's arrival as the "second coming," which didn't make him very happy I presume, but this was just another thing, this was just going to solve all the problems; see, everything was going to solve all the problems. . . .

We expected the psychiatrist to be a salesman, a super public relations man and so on; and nobody is. As a matter of fact, we jokingly used to talk about what we need is a beer salesman on this Board, I mean, we ought to get some guy who is really, you know, he's convinced it's the thing, although he knows nothing about it, and he goes back and tells everybody else.

I knew we were in financial trouble by that time; I think the board did too; but we had felt that if we could hold on a year with this new director who would have standing in the community, this area, that we would begin to have more patients and the institution would be able to carry on; and that with a new director we might then begin to get outside funds for support for research, residency training, and then a possibility that we might begin to accumulate money through gifts.

I know this, that there was a feeling—I don't know whether it was completely warranted—that he would attract greater support for the hospital, support not only at a clinical level but maybe at a financial level. That he individually might be the individual whom we could go down to Rotary with, for instance, and present the story of Crest Foundation to the leading businessmen and industrialists and all the rest in the city. I presume we were patterning our thinking somewhat after Menningers, and that he as a professional man could better bring the story to these people than we as lay people could. Hopefully, then, we on the board would follow up after he had created the necessary interest in these people that they would possibly divert some of their giving from something else to this thing as being worthwhile.

Soon, then, Dr. Doren and the board were trying to find some money. At his first board meeting, in September, 1959, Doren emphasized that the fundamental question regarding Crest was its existence, in terms of the financial problem. By October, the fund-raising committee of the board recommended hiring a full-time professional fund raiser. The board decided to write to "appropriate Foundations having funds available for which Crest might be eligible."

In November, Dr. Doren wrote his view of the "Current and Projected Development and Needs of the Crest Foundation Hospital." This note, which was to serve as an aid to the fund raisers on the board, was characteristic of Dr. Doren's attempts to define a new and solid direction for Crest. His presentations were undramatic. In this report, he described Crest as unique in its degree of individualized patient treatment on a relationship and total environmental basis. In giving "a brief description of the financial basis of the hospital operation," he noted that

> . . . cost per patient is high because of the number of specialized staff needed to carry out the hospital's philosophy of individualized treatment. In order to make the cost to the patient as low as possible, the expense of new construction and major repairs and replacements have not been included in patient fees, but contributions are sought to cover this deficit.

He commented that there were necessary "basic additions and repairs to the buildings and grounds" which would require $25,000. Also, "in order that such high quality of specialized treatment facilities should be available to not only well-to-do patients, a fund must be established to provide care at less than cost." The full cost endowment per bed per year would be approximately $12,000. He suggested a reasonable yearly budget for a research program of $16,000, of which a certain portion might be provided by research grants. The training of one psychiatric resident and two psychiatric nurses, costing $13,000, of which about $9,000 might be expected from public health stipends, was a minimal training program. Doren conceived of the training program as including three residents, four psychiatric nurses, a social worker, and a psychologist. The cost for this number of personnel would be $48,000 per year, of which about $34,000 might be available from public health stipends. Doren also recommended adding five more beds. His reasoning was as follows:

With our present 30 bed capacity it was expected that in this current atypical year the average census would be low, 23 patients. With our present basic staff and operational costs this would leave a deficit of $52,000 at the end of the year. It is expected, however, that our average census will gradually rise to slightly over 27, which is the maximum number to be expected within our present structure. At this patient census with our present staff the deficit would be $18,000 per year. However, with an average census of 27 patients we would need additional staff, one psychiatrist and two psychiatric aides for providing optimal service. With this census of 27 and the additional staff the deficit would be $35,000 per year. However, with the above described additional staff it would be possible to care for more than 27 patients, near 32 or 33. So with 33 patients and the additional staff it is estimated that clinical operation would be self-sustaining, that is, there would be little or no deficit per year. In order to increase the hospital's capacity and efficiency so as to have an average census of 32 or 33 patients, structural modifications and additions would be necessary to the extent of adding five more beds. The cost of this addition would be $30,000.

It is noteworthy that this memorandum, like the rest of Dr. Doren's organized presentations to the board, never was formally considered. The board continued to be preoccupied with the financial problem, concerning itself with the hiring of a fund raiser. It spent its November meeting in "what turned out to be a rather protracted discussion concerning the selection of a person to work for the Crest Foundation in a fund-raising capacity." "It was agreed that such a person should be selected as soon as possible, and before the next Board meeting." On December 17, Miss Susan Lane was engaged for this position.

Miss Lane stated:

It was never really defined as anything, it was kind of defined—we need help and we think you're the one who

> can help us. They thought that they needed to be known around the community a little more. They felt they needed to interest some more influential people in what was going on. . . . We need to think about raising some money, do you think we can raise money? . . . Other organizations raise money, so I said, sure, you can raise money. It was not defined; they didn't know what they wanted; they wanted help. . . . I was also to save things. First, I think, Dr. Doren was going to save things. I don't know who was going to save things before him.

She later commented:

> I sort of started horsing around a little bit. Public relations is, as I'm sure you're aware, an exceedingly indefinite field anyway, I mean, what you do is you look at the situation and you try to decide well would this be good here and as I recall, I realized immediately, they needed everything.

Miss Lane, hired three months after Dr. Doren's arrival, noted that the board was looking to her as a saviour. The board's high hopes in Doren as a money-raiser had quickly vanished. A number of the board members concentrated their concern on the census, which had not risen sufficiently. For the month of September—the month Doren arrived—the average census had been 21 patients. The average census for October was 23.1; for November, 24.4; and for December, 23.6. There had been a slight increase, but it was not one which could make a real difference. Expenses had risen considerably. The professional staff, very costly to the hospital, were bringing in little psychotherapy money. Dr. Doren's salary was quite large compared with the salaries that had been paid previously; and in his getting-acquainted period, he was doing little money-earning psychotherapy. Dr. Preston had cut down on his therapy load since he had been doing all the hospital management of patients; thus, his earnings were minimal.

One board member stated that the enthusiasm about Doren decreased because of the census. "Gee, that census just simply could not get up there." He said that Doren should have brought "results." "He's getting the money. He should help earn it."

Another noted retrospectively:

> I had the feeling, the impression—I'm again reflecting the attitude of others—that there had been quite a resurgence of hope when Doren took it over, and that this was like getting a new driver for the Greyhound bus: after a while you find out there are the same number of stop lights and so forth, and so this feeling of freshness tends to diminish. I think people tend in a situation like that—particularly one where there was this aura of futility to start—immediately to idealize this new executive figure, and then to find out that he is human after all; so you go up, and then maybe you go down a little further than you were when you started.

Another "felt very deeply that . . . if there was one thing that could save Crest it was a really fiery and dedicated . . . fellow." He continued:

> From the beginning, I had this uneasy feeling that without the kind of a person I have described, the game was close to being lost, and I saw nothing in what Doren did to persuade me that we had such a man. I don't think that this was the general board attitude. I would say that the general board attitude was that he was, as I felt, professionally competent, and he was here to do a job to the best of his ability and that he wanted to communicate with the board and wanted to get oriented properly with the staff. . . . It was such a relief to have a director.

Thus, like the staff at the hospital, the board members began with high hopes which in a relatively short time were deflated. After three to four months, as the new year began, Dr. Doren no longer fitted their needs. They searched for new saviours and continued this search till the end. They found places to rest their hopes, suddenly and desperately, only to be acutely disappointed, time and again.

The third wing, the consultants, also were involved in the

crisis. The problem of Crest's financial difficulty—it was reported that the hospital "is operating at a deficit of $3,000 to $4,000 per month"—could not, after all, be separated from the "census," which was related to the problem of referrals from the local psychiatrists. The local psychiatrists were not making many referrals. A new board member insisted that in this time of crisis all board and consulting staff members should contribute financially to Crest. Thus, when the consultants were faced with contributing money to Crest, the appropriateness of which they questioned, the problem of referrals necessarily arose. The October, 1959, minutes of the consulting staff state:

> Discussion about the Consulting Staff's making contributions of a financial nature to the hospital led to some discussion about the hospital's census and need for more referrals of patients. Along this line, there was discussion as to whether there was a sufficient market for the type of treatment that Crest has to offer, whether physicians on the Consulting Staff who were hospitalizing patients at hospitals other than Crest were actually supporting Crest, whether other sources of referrals of patients that would profit from treatment of Crest might be sought out, and whether the treatment philosophy of Crest should be altered so as to allow for the treatment of shorter-term patients. These questions were discussed back and forth in a limited fashion with no particular conclusions being reached. The president of the Consulting Staff indicated that there would be more formal study of these questions.

Such criticism of Crest was not new, and had been voiced from time to time by various members of the psychiatric community. By and large, however, the consulting staff as a group had supported the conception of Crest. That is, they had theoretically backed the philosophy, ideology, and methods of treatment at Crest. As a consequence of the October discussion, the president of the consulting staff appointed a committee "to investigate whether changes should be made at Crest and whether Crest is serving its proper place in the psychiatric community." The committee was comprised of the major critics of the philosophy of

Crest, those who questioned "psychoanalytic" hospital treatment, as well as ex-Crest psychiatrists and supporters of the Crest philosophy. The positions were about evenly distributed.

This committee reported at the consulting staff meeting of January 15, 1960, in the midst of the suicide epidemic, and without knowledge of the deterioration in clinical functioning at the hospital. The committee had met twice with Dr. Doren. The report reads in part:

> The membership of the committee had presented to Dr. Doren a wide variety of views about how the hospital appeared to be functioning. These views included several critical comments. The question was raised whether the milieu program at Crest had been overrated as to its importance in the treatment program and the results of treatment. There were opinions that there had been an unreasonable exclusion of non-psychological treatment measures such as drugs, electric shock therapy and even other psychological treatment measures that were not strictly psychoanalytical. There were opinions that equally good results were obtained in other hospitals that did not have a formal milieu program and the question was raised as to whether the costs of this milieu program were justified.

> It was suggested that the hospital be open to psychiatrists other than those on the full-time professional staff of the hospital and that these other psychiatrists conduct the management of patients at the hospital. This would in effect make Crest much more of an open hospital than it is now. It was also suggested that in the light of the census being consistently below capacity that a reduced rate be made for some patients who could not otherwise afford Crest, so that the hospital beds would be filled. And it was suggested the treatment measures in general be broadened.

> These comments were answered in part at the first meeting. It was pointed out that in terms of results, it was important to remember that many patients at Crest were

chronically ill people who had been treatment failures at other hospitals. For example, many patients at Crest had had long and frequent series of electric shock therapy earlier in their illness.

Dr. Doren pointed out that recently there had been some broadening of the treatment measures at Crest. Actually several patients are in therapy with various members of consulting staff and he emphasized that Crest is not in competition with other psychiatric hospitals in the area, that along with its formal milieu program it is a different kind of hospital. The main point was that Crest is something different, something unique, that it was not trying to be another psychiatric sanitarium, similar to those already in existence and that while these questions about the hospital should be evaluated from the viewpoint of eventual changes, to do so at this time would be destructive to the integrity of the hospital.

As to financial factors, Dr. Doren stated that at a census of 23 patients the hospital still operates at a deficit. When the average census reaches 27, another physician will be needed which in turn though would enable five additional beds to be added and a census of 32 or 33 to be reached. This would be optimum both from the standpoint of treatment and finances.

The Committee's report concluded with the recommendation that Dr. Doren's position of no changes in the hospital at the present time be supported. . . .

Thus, in the face of extensive criticism of Crest by the consulting staff committee, Dr. Doren presented himself as fully in support of the old identity—"Crest is something different, something unique," and spoke of its milieu program as a significant aspect which could not be changed if the hospital was to retain its integrity.

It was in the context then, of acute clinical disturbance at the hospital, active criticism by the consulting staff, and great financial concern on the part of the members of the board, that Doren's summary report to the board was given on January 28,

1960. As in his dealings with the consulting staff, Doren attempted to draw a picture of Crest as a hospital which, although momentarily at a low ebb, continued to exhibit a potential for vigor and vitality, and to be capable of a special role in psychiatry. Dr. Doren's early observations appear at the beginning of this chapter. The remainder follow:

> By mid-December the census had gradually increased. There were almost twice as many admissions as in the same quarter the previous year. There were also more discharged, so the average census was not considerably higher. The morale of the staff had increased to its highest point and there was a feeling of confidence and coordination in the atmosphere. In the next four weeks (December 23–January 20) there was a series of clinical difficulties and complications which were very upsetting to the staff. Had their morale not reached the high peak that it had prior to these difficulties, I feel that the staff would have been literally demoralized. As it was, they dealt very well and effectively with the situations and have regained their confidence to a considerable degree.
>
> AT THIS TIME WE ARE AT THE CRITICAL POINT. WE MUST EITHER GO AHEAD AND PROVIDE WHAT IS NEEDED TO MAKE CREST A GOOD HOSPITAL, CONSISTENT WITH ITS IDEALS— OR WE MUST RECOGNIZE THAT THIS IS NOT POSSIBLE AND THUS BEAT A RETREAT IN THE BEST POSSIBLE ORDER. In other words, Crest might have to change, and could this be done so that Crest would survive as "Crest"? Would we want it to?
>
> In the past ten years of Crest's existence its general welfare has run in cycles of fairly good to bad. The height of prosperity seemed to have been reached in about 1957. However it seems that no solid plateau has ever been reached, at least not financially. It is likely that the operation of Crest will always involve a deficit. THEREFORE, THE MONIES RAISED SHOULD BE NOT ONLY IN VIEW OF FULFILLING OUR IMMEDIATE, EMERGENCY NEEDS,

BUT ALSO THAT THE CIRCLE OF INTEREST IN CREST BE OF SUCH A NATURE THAT CONTRIBUTED FUNDS WILL ALWAYS BE COMING IN.

A statement of what I wish as a program for Crest is in order. In general terms it can be very simply stated. I would wish Crest to be a hospital wherein any patient could be carefully and well evaluated and could receive whatever treatment and care would be the most effective in alleviating his suffering and re-establishing his health. Basic to treatment is always to be the relationship and activities program in all aspects. However, if and when other therapies are indicated to further the patient's comfort and recovery, they will be used adjunctively.

In this basic setting training will be provided for psychiatric residents, nurses, aides, and for social workers and psychologists. Research should prosper in such a setting.

From the present situation of Crest at its lowest ebb, time will be needed to rebuild its program and its more solid base of operation. This may be a matter of two or three years.

HOWEVER, THE NEEDS DESCRIBED CANNOT WAIT. EFFECTIVE ACTION IS NECESSARY NOW. THE QUESTION IS—CAN THE AMOUNT OF MONEY NECESSARY FOR THESE NEEDS BE RAISED? ARE ALL CONCERNED WITH RAISING IT WILLING TO WORK TOWARD THIS GOAL? IF THE ANSWER TO THESE QUESTIONS IS "NO," I THINK WE MUST REALIZE THAT AT THIS TIME AND ACT ACCORDING TO THIS REALITY.

He then detailed an elaborate program of expansion. This program involved the hiring of an additional psychiatrist, more nurses and aides, additional buildings, new furniture, improvement of recreational facilities, etc. Furthermore, he proposed fully endowed free beds and a large-scale training program. With regard to financing this program, he noted that:

Until the bed capacity is expanded to 35 and until the census would reach an average of 32 or 33, a deficit of approximately $35,000 annually should be expected. Not including the deficit, the amount needed is $121,000. With the deficit this would amount to $156,000.

At the same meeting Miss Lane presented her plan for raising money. The first contributors were to be members of the board and consulting staff. Following this, there was to be a "big gift" campaign. Miss Lane had organized a list of "40 to 100 of the richest men in town" to be approached. She noted that her money-raising plan was based on Dr. Doren's figures. Her program "was designed to carry the hospital until such time as capital improvements could be made to expand the bed capacity" to the point when "according to Doren's figures, the thing would be self-sustaining."

The board's response to the presentation of these reports was striking:

> After lengthy discussion of both of the above reports, the Board agreed that 100 per cent financial contribution from the Board and the Consulting Staff was of the utmost importance. It was also agreed by the Board that a pep talk of the inspirational variety for the Board and the Consulting Staff every year might help to keep enthusiasm at a high pitch.
>
> It was agreed that meetings of the Board be held weekly for the "duration of the emergency."

The board clearly felt helpless; its request for yearly "inspirational" pep talks seems totally incongruous. The decision to meet weekly for the "duration of the emergency," apparently appropriate action, was not carried out. In retrospect, Dr. Doren's report with its perhaps overwhelming figure of $156,000 as a necessity, seems to have had the result of discouraging the board, rather than its intended effect of presenting a challenge.

Shortly following this meeting, Miss Lane resigned her position. She later stated:

> We sat down to a meeting one night, and I had had pledge cards made—I went that far—and I sat down at the board meeting with names of people to solicit for money, and nothing ever happened, nobody ever talked to any-

body. Nobody was pushing. They really didn't know what they wanted, you see, and they expected somebody to come along and do it for them.

But shortly following Miss Lane's resignation, a new hope for the board appeared. William Bender, a young, alert businessman, became interested in Crest through a friend who was a board member. He was invited to a board meeting and he came with ideas. Bender described his plan as follows:

> I very shortly tried to develop a scheme whereby they could sell, for lack of a better term, industrial charitable beds, on the theory that this was a means of giving industry locally some feeling of tangible reward, or some opportunity could be made tangible for their contributing to the maintenance of the hospital. And as I recall, I think I made up a four-or-five-page written statement which was supposed to be sort of a sales piece. Well, in any case, I wrote that with a view toward trying to sell industry and other large givers in the community on the idea that this is something that somebody needed to do something about—since there are very few business firms of any consequence that do not have people from time to time who need this kind of care—and that they could thus purchase this bed on an individual basis which would be made available to straight charity patients at a time when it was not being utilized by someone from a given company; and this was with the thought that if a company employing, say, four or five hundred people were to buy a bed, which I think was about $10,000, the chances of its using it were perhaps one out of ten; and in effect this bed would be available for use throughout the year for charitable purposes.

Many of the board members found his statement very helpful and extremely important. It buoyed them up with hope once again; a hope, however, which was short-lived inasmuch as they were unable to implement Bender's plans. Bender's statement considered the history of psychiatric treatment, emphasizing the growth of professional hopefulness in the treatment of mental patients. It read, in part:

> These fundamental changes—in the capacity of medical science to treat the psychiatric patient, and in our attitudes toward the need for making treatment available to those who most need it—have brought with them a challenge of considerable magnitude. It may be simply stated as follows:
>
> > "We have a need to establish *standards of excellence* of treatment—'lighthouses' if you will, for the psychiatric profession. . . .
> >
> > "Without an institution which strives to be a model treatment center for a geographic region, standards of true excellence for the psychiatric profession in that area will fail of establishment. Without such an institution, the public hospitals for care and treatment of the mentally ill will fail to lift their own standards from the level of mediocrity. Without an institution in which the private psychiatrist may place his patients for specialized, round-the-clock care, the area will fail in the long run to attract its quota of the most competent psychiatrists."

The statement goes on to point out that institutions for the mentally ill do not elicit the financial support attracted by institutions caring for the physically ill, and emphasizes that the growth of Crest is dependent upon the people of the region. The rationale ends:

> It is our purpose in making this statement to ask you, or your organization, to subscribe funds for free beds in the Crest Hospital. The establishment of six free beds, at $12,000 annually is intended to serve three purposes; (1) to provide the highest quality of treatment in a model institution for the mentally ill to some members of the community who would otherwise be unable to afford such treatment; (2) to assure the continued existence of The Crest Foundation; and (3) to contribute materially

to Crest's capacity to accomplish research and training in psychiatry. . . .

We would like to ask one more thing: that you arrange with one of us to make a visit to Crest. We would like nothing better than to have you walk through our buildings and talk with members of the hospital staff—to see with your own eyes that Crest is a place in which people who are mentally sick may become well.

If you should make such a visit, you will want to come back again—with a hammer and nails—to help Crest build for the future of this community.

One can understand the enthusiasm with which the tired board greeted this well conceived and concrete plan, which presented the image of Crest as special, as a "model institution." But in spite of the board's positive response, it was to fail. Bender noted:

My principal observation was that the members of the board were looking for somebody else to solve their problems, so I came in like a large wind from Winnetka, as the saying goes, and presented this scheme; it was all written out and all the i's were dotted and the t's were crossed, and so they could sit there and say gee whiz this looks pretty good, it looks like it will raise some money and all very nicely worded and Bill, aren't you a marvelous writer. And so I said, okay, now all that is necessary is for you to make a list of the twenty largest givers in Columbia from an industrial standpoint and divide them up among you and go out and sell this. And there was a lot of mumbling and so forth, but finally some people agreed to take some company names and go at this. Now only one I know really made any effort—I think there were two. The others, to the best of my knowledge, did not.

Bender added:

There was, yes, this sense of futility, but they came to these board meetings with almost a passionate sense of desperation, and this I think was one reason why this little scheme of mine was so well received, because they had no other alternative.

Retrospectively, board members discerned many reasons for their failure to attempt to "sell" Crest even with the periodic boosts and revivals of hope. They felt that the community saw Crest as a hospital for wealthy patients. This was certainly true; the fee was over $1,000 a month, and psychotherapy costs were additional. Moreover, the board members sensed that there was no consistent support in the psychiatric community for the view that Crest was a worthwhile institution. This was essentially a product of the split in the psychiatric community, which supported the hospital so ambivalently. Beyond this, the board members had no figures to support the contention that Crest was doing good work. Thus, they found themselves without any substantial basis for hope, or enthusiasm.

The following statements are illustrative:

> There were too many people of means who felt that Crest was only for the rich, and the rich could take care of themselves. If they were going to make contributions for the benefit of society, they wanted to do it for those who were unable to finance their own treatment. So that created quite an obstacle or hurdle to overcome.

> I would say the single factor that alarmed me most was an apparent lack of solidarity between the hospital and the psychiatric community; this was very confusing to me, and I personally felt that the hospital, if it was worthy of support, it was worthy of support by the psychiatrists and the rest in the area here that were working in the same field. In our contacts with the consulting staff my impression was that there was not a solidarity among this group as to how the hospital should go, or where it should go, or what was wrong with it; and therefore we had nothing to hang our hat on, to say, well, I think we are on the right track.

> One other thing that just killed me—I hardly could get over it—was when we had the discussion of research as to

whether Crest had helped anyone. . . . We had categorically asked the question, well, how do you prepare some criteria for telling the public? I mean the lay guys, you know, that want to know. How do you go about telling them that you've got something, that you can do something, that you can help these people? . . . They said there are no criteria. . . . Scientifically you can't say this and this and this made this guy better. . . . I would say at that point, you might as well turn the key in the door of any social agency. . . . I guess if a book were written on what not to tell a board, don't get the board out of its field with any of these real precise scientific reports. This gets a board way out yonder somewhere. . . . And at the same time I think you can be very truthful with a board; you can give them everything they need to know that they can understand.

The helplessness and discouragement of the board was manifested in ways other than the difficulty in raising money. For example, the new board president, a relatively new member elected to office in the spring, stated:

I was most reluctant, obviously, and I said "no," first. I said no, I wouldn't do it. In the first place, I thought I was the wrong person, I didn't have the contact with anybody that would do this group any good. I mean, it was a question of nobody wanted the job, not that I'm a martyr type, but somebody had to do it, so I had no desire to be president—it wasn't something that people were fighting for, I'll tell you that.

In May, the board hired a professional fund raiser who had been highly recommended. Unfortunately he could not join the staff until September. Some of the board members continued to work hard; but little was accomplished.

The July minutes read:

Dr. Doren outlined his views as to the needed growth of Crest and improvements and changes which should be planned for during the next year. He states that he would mimeograph his views for distribution to the Board. Among his views were that Crest needs an additional psychiatrist, a psychiatrist for research, two residents and should have training for two students, two graduate nurses and three representatives from state hospital staffs. He further felt that a free bed should be established now and a free bed or beds should be furnished by endowment of $6,000 a year on which there should be no gain, but also no loss. He felt the new building should be completed within the next year, that a new Wing would be desirable, that a night care unit with 8 beds at a cost of perhaps $30,000 would be useful for patients who needed minimum care and could probably bring in a 10% return at a much lower monthly rate than the regular patients.

No discussion of this plan took place at the board meeting. The plan was presented to the consulting staff the following day. The consulting staff minutes note:

> Dr. Doren concluded his remarks by indicating that if the objectives indicated could not be reasonably far along in a reasonable time, then consideration would have to be given to closing the hospital. There followed an active discussion with questions to Dr. Doren on his proposals regarding the day unit and the night unit. Some scepticism was expressed by several members on the financial soundness of the plans. Dr. Doren indicated he would welcome specific suggestions. The question was raised about the financial status of Crest at the present time and Dr. Doren indicated there were still difficulties, but he anticipated that these would be overcome.

Again, Dr. Doren was making an effort, presenting a plan. As in his January report, he stressed that the hospital had to aspire, that the board and the consulting staff had to get involved and act, or Crest should close. But, as before, the challenge was not accepted. Many considered that the plan was too grand, and was thus inappropriate. The board was concerned about immediate finances, about keeping the hospital alive. By August, the financial situation was deemed to be critical. On August 11, 1960, a special meeting of the Board of Trustees was held, to which neither Dr. Doren nor Mr. Hanson, the hospital administrator, was invited. At that meeting:

> Mr. Bone stated that he had understood from Mr. Hanson the census of the hospital was 17 and that there were no pending applications. He was further advised that there would be a need of $5,000 on August 15 and another $8,000 by August 25. There was a discussion as to the reason for the low census. The question was raised as to whether difficult patients were being turned down and whether, if all the patients were difficult or hopeless, the purpose of Crest would be fulfilled. It was pointed out that if the facts as presently understood were correct, we would need approximately $30,000 through December of 1960, even if there was an increase in the census at the rate of one a month.
>
> Mr. Blair moved that in view of the financial situation the Board should advise the Medical Director that it recommends closure unless the Medical Director will submit changes in the program which will give the Board confidence that a need is being provided for and will give reasonable probability of adequate financing.
>
> There was a discussion at which all agreed that this matter should be discussed with the Medical Director first and then with a committee of the Consulting Staff so that the Board would be fully advised of the possibilities.
>
> The difficulties of closing such an institution and its obligations to the community to continue if it is of value were discussed at length. Possible alternatives of changes in operation were discussed.
>
> On motion duly made and seconded, it was resolved that the Executive Committee . . . be authorized to make such investigation and take such steps as might be considered necessary.

Following this meeting the president of the Board of Trustees called Dr. Plant, acting chairman of the consulting staff. Dr. Plant reported to the consulting staff that the president on this occasion informed him that: "Crest was in the most serious financial crisis of its history and the Board had decided to consider the possibility of closing the hospital. He urgently requested that I call together within the next 24 to 48 hours a representative group of consultants in order to discuss the crisis and to make recommendations concerning the position of the hospital."

A group of consultants met on August 13. Prior to the conference Dr. Doren had called Dr. Plant and "made himself available to be contacted if we wished any advice or communication with him that evening during our meeting." Doren also said that he felt "the crisis was not as severe as it was felt to be by the board since the census had already begun to rise and would be 20 or 21 within a few days according to the outlook on Wednesday." He felt that his plans for the future still held in his own mind and he wished to recommend that the hospital continue in its present status.

At the meeting, Crest's financial problems were presented. The consultant staff set forth two unanimous recommendations:

> First, that the present operation at Crest be discontinued. There were a number of bases for this recommendation varying among the individuals but they ranged from the impossibility of the community to support such an expensive hospital; the fact that the consultants who had hospital patients were very often unable to use the hospital; financial crisis had followed financial crisis until the present one was so severe as to warrant no further efforts at least in the same direction; Dr. Doren, instead of shrinking the operation and cost of the hospital, had begun to expand it again and this was questioned strongly by some of the members of the committee.

> The second unanimous recommendation was that, if it could be shown that the community needed a good open psychiatric hospital, the board be urged to go in this direction with the hospital. Hopefully Crest would have a full time psychiatrist on the staff to coordinate hospital activities and to treat out of state patients, etc. The doc-

tors who would bring their patients there would consist of consulting staff members only and if necessary the consulting staff would be expanded to include other psychiatrists who would meet the approval of the present consulting staff.

The report continued:

The question arose as to whether the present consulting staff would be able to support the hospital to a sufficient extent to warrant continuation. One of the problems which has beset Crest from the beginning has been the moral support from the analysts as well as the leadership of the consultant staff by the analysts, who however have been unable to send more than a handful of patients to the hospital because of the nature of their office practices. It was felt that if the proposed change takes place at Crest that the nature of the consulting staff should change drastically and control of the consulting staff should pass from the analytic group to those people who at least have some hospital practice.

In terms of expanding the second recommendation in order to make it workable several suggestions were made. For one thing, it was felt that a resident psychiatrist would be very helpful in maintaining staff morale and in coordinating the overall treatment program. He could also treat out of town patients who might be referred directly to the hospital. His salary could be absorbed in part by his own psychotherapy or charges to patients and an additional small amount per week which would spread over all the patient's fees. It was hoped that Dr. Preston might be interested in such a position if the recommendations were accepted by the board.

It was recognized that there would have to be a marked paring of cost at the hospital and with this in mind the group felt that it might well be possible to cut the staff considerably so that the services offered were still adequate and yet the number of staff people was not as high as it is at the present time.

Some mention was made of the large number of suicides during the past year at Crest and this was brought into the discussion as a possible problem. It was felt by the group, however, that it did not have a place in the discussion since it lay more in the area of the hospital treatment program.

At the end of the meeting, which lasted for approximately two hours, it was decided to make the two above recommendations to the Board of Trustees and to appoint a sub-committee to meet with the Board of Trustees the following night.

The joint meeting suggested by the consultants was held the following evening, and the above recommendations were then presented to the board. It is noteworthy that both recommendations foresaw the death of Crest *qua* Crest. This was not new thinking on the part of many of the consultants. In their January report, the changes included in the second recommendation were made explicit. The views presented were not those of all the professional consultants. One stated that in his opinion opening the hospital to members of the consulting staff would have meant chaos.

It is also noteworthy that neither of the consultants' recommendations left any place for Dr. Doren at Crest. At the joint meeting of the board and the consultant staff, while Crest was roundly criticized, Dr. Doren was directly attacked. The president of the board recalled:

> I mean it was so obvious to everybody that we've got to all work together here, and we had one of the meetings . . . which is the damndest thing I ever attended. This was the final blow. . . . One man [a senior analyst] ripped the thing up and said it was a country club operation and he wasn't even sure the theory was any good you know, just grind right into the group. And these guys all sat around and we asked pointedly now is this what you think—uh huh, yeah. The next day I think three people talked to me, called up and said well now it isn't really this bad, we think it's a great club and all this

and that, and Joe was a little off base. . . . At this stage,
I mean, I concluded that there was absolutely no hope.
. . . I don't think there was any support [for Crest]
from anybody. The next day there was some but what the
hell good is this going to do. . . . [The analyst] who
made the speech didn't ever backtrack, but some of his
colleagues did.

Another board member believed that this meeting ended what
rapport, if any, had existed between the consulting staff and the
board. He added:

We had this meeting, and it was brought out that there
had been three or four suicides, and the one faction spoke
very strongly on this and really condemned him openly.
. . . They were talking about Dr. Doren.

The suicides were the central point in the attack on Doren.
One of the consultants, speaking of the meeting and the suicides,
stated:

This is often cited as evidence that things weren't right
out there in people's minds, and someone would say, at a
meeting with the board present, if I had these suicides on
my hands, I would be in analysis in ten minutes won-
dering what am I doing. So this may be a good thought,
but I don't think it's a good one to say to the board.

An officer of the consulting staff later recalled:

Then we had a meeting with the board . . . and at that
meeting the scene changed and became much more sort
of anti-Doren. . . . And later I had to go around and
patch this up, and point out that the actual consulting
staff did not feel this way, this was a few people's opinion—but really our opinion was we don't know him.

A familiar pattern had once more been repeated. An individual closely involved with Crest gave this ironic account of the
reactions of the consultants to successive medical directors:

Well it was a very similar pattern [concerning the medical director]. These men were all thought of before they

came, and as they assumed the directorship, as being full of promise. These were men who were analytically oriented or analysts, who were intelligent, leaders, able to run the hospital, able to get along with the consulting staff, able to satisfy the board's requirements; in short these were men of the hour each time. Everybody agreed. The consultants, the board, the public, everybody, even the governor for all I know—but everybody agreed that each of these men was the man who was going to do the job. Then there was a period of honeymoon. . . . The consultants having their meetings [were asking] should we stay together, we are not needed; Dr. Davidson— Dunn—Doren is so good that, we really, I wonder if we are needed; we'll be an advisory board; we'll just sit here and let him run the hospital the way he sees fit. Are we lucky! We've got this great place in town with this wonderful fellow. Then, the creeping dissatisfaction: Say what's he up to out there? I heard from my patient that an aide is taking morphine every morning or something, you know. Oh well, that's nothing, that's not important. And then—say that medical director, where did he get his ideas from, you know, and what's the trouble? And a creeping dissatisfaction, where's the money? These guys, I thought they had referrals, they have got [empty] beds out there, you know. . . . How come he's still with the hospital? Well, personally, you know, he's pretty disturbed, he's a neurotic guy, sick . . . I'm parodying. With the ultimate being: what's happened to Crest? With the really positive people saying "We've got to help them. That Doren, that Dunn, that Davidson, they've gone off their rocker, where do they think they are? Topeka or Chestnut Lodge! Where did they get these grandiose ideas? They haven't got any money; they're going broke and they want to do all this stuff! They're nuts! They're sick! This isn't the same guy we hired for the job. This man is crazy. Something must have happened to him."

In spite of the crisis, Dr. Doren continued. He was still the director, even though the proposals that had been made left no place for him. He did not deal with this problem directly, and continued to make his recommendations for the future of Crest. On August 22, 1960, he sent a report to the consulting staff for its consideration. He noted that the material had been written two weeks before, on August 7: "However our recent financial crisis occurred, and considering the nature of the reaction to that, I decided to delay the distribution of this material." The "material," however, had not been changed.

Doren's report noted that in his last presentation of views before the consulting staff, "I emphasized that the attitude toward Crest should be more in reference to its growth than to its mere existence. It is obvious, however, that it cannot grow unless it does exist."

> The purpose of this communication is to review some of the facets of the now-considered plan for Crest's development. Members of the consulting staff will therefore have the opportunity to think about them prior to the more detailed discussion of them in the appropriate committee.

The plans presented, however, scarcely differed from those in Doren's July 1, report. Some additions—some possible changes—follow:

> At this time we are seriously considering how it might be possible to vary the fees charged to patients in accordance with the cost of the care which they require. For example, for patients who require the maximum amount of care such as on the closed section, the fee would be highest. For patients in the intermediate section who require less intensive care, a lower ratio of personnel per patient, the cost might be basically somewhat less. In the partial hospital section, the new service and building referred to above, the cost might be even further reduced. By means of this variable fee, the total cost of hospitalization could be reduced considerably. For example, at

present a patient in the hospital for six months would have to pay $6,600, exclusive of psychotherapy, whereas on the variable fee system it might be possible for him to reduce this amount to half or even less.

Though it is still premature to initiate the practice, I hope that in the not-too-distant future it will be possible to have psychiatrists practicing in the community bring their patients to Crest and manage and treat them here as their own patients. Many factors have to be considered prior to trying this change of policy.

One consulting staff member reflected on part of this proposal:

Doren had in mind at one time to set up a half-way house. I thought a half-way house was a terrific idea, and something that we could really use in Columbia, and I had in mind several times myself to set up a half-way house. Well he brought this idea up and I said, how can you think of terms of—I don't know how much money it was necessary to spend to do this—$20,000 or $30,000 to get it going; and if we can't get Crest to go, Crest is crashing around our ears, how can we start off and spend something else?

The hospital professional staff, to whom the plans also were presented, were equally distressed. The atmosphere at the hospital had not changed. In May, the professional staff began to meet, to attempt to discuss the tensions that existed between them, and to talk particularly about the group of suicides that had occurred early in January. The meetings were not very successful. They turned into a general criticism of the director, who was present, with complaints about the difficulty in communicating with him. In spite of the direct expression of these feelings, positive results were not forthcoming.

One of the participants noted:

I think we all felt that many subjects have had to—particularly the suicides, they being a very hot subject, painful one—have had to wait, pending some kind of a getting together to work them out. They were terrific blows, the suicides, of course. I feel that the insecurity resulting perhaps largely from them was permeating the whole hospital, and that they must have been a terrific blow to Doren, and his anxiety was mounting, and that somehow everybody's security to the furthest corner of the hospital was being mobilized, and that perhaps it was the transmitting of it from the top of the pyramid. I felt somehow that as all of us dealt directly with this anxiety, we came away less confident, rather than more.

In June, Mrs. Irwin escaped and word of her suicide was received while Dr. Doren was away on a trip. Dr. Carpenter was the acting director, and the professional staff went to Carpenter to talk about its total discouragement with Crest and with Dr. Doren. Dr. Carpenter expressed his feeling at the time—and the professional staff agreed—that the most appropriate thing to do was to close the hospital. By the time Dr. Doren presented his plans, in the latter part of August, discouragement at the hospital had become chronic. Both Dr. Preston and Miss Nelson had offered their resignations. Dr. Paulson, although he had not resigned, had spoken of resigning. Hopelessness was endemic.

The continuing financial crisis brought the climax. On September 16, at a board meeting, "The desperate financial situation facing Crest" was outlined. "Mr. Hanson reported that $6,000 was needed by Friday, September 19, in order to meet the payroll." At this meeting, too, the new fund raiser presented a money-raising program. He had come earlier in the month of September; but it was clearly too late for his services to avail.

Doren proposed two major policy changes both of which were approved unanimously by the board and announced to the consulting staff in a memorandum. The first change was setting up an "open staff." "Psychiatrists on the consulting staff may now admit patients to Crest and care for them as their own hospital patients with respect to management and treatment."

The second change of policy concerned the provision of four beds at a fee less than the cost of their maintenance. . . . The now available less than cost four beds will be at the rate of $150 per week, but additional charges will be made for other than basic service and activities.

The statement ended:

This change is considered as the first step toward the attainment of an ultimate goal wherein any person might be considered for admission to Crest, regardless of his financial circumstances. His fee would be based upon his ability to pay. If this goal can be reached, it will require time and considerable community support.

The board had borrowed $5,000 the previous month, but by payday, Friday, September 19, 1960, money was not available to meet the payroll. On that day, a professional staff meeting was called, at five o'clock in the afternoon. Dr. Doren stated that there was not enough money to meet the payroll, and that the probability was that Crest would have to close, short of a miracle. The rest of the staff group felt that Crest ought to close, miracle or no.

On Sunday afternoon, September 21, 1960, a special meeting of the board was held:

[The president] advised that there was not enough cash on hand to meet the payroll for the preceding Friday and that although the trustees had solicited commitments from initial contributors during the last few days there were not enough commitments to make it practical to continue to operate.

Dr. Doren advised that two of the key employees, Joan Nelson, Head Nurse, and Dr. Preston, had given notice that they would terminate their employment, and that because of the uncertainty of the situation there was some tension among the staff which left no choice but to close operation.

Mr. Hanson estimated total obligations through September 30, 1960, would be approximately $60,000 in addition to the $32,000 first mortgage, which included some $12,700 payroll, $11,600 accrued vacation, $10,000 accounts payable, $13,300 in notes and other obligations.

He stated that accounts receivable were not substantial and that inventory was approximately $8,000.

On motion duly made and seconded, it was unanimously resolved by those present that the hospital operations should discontinue as soon as possible, giving first regard to the patients' welfare, second to the employees, and third to other creditors.

Crest's closing was announced to the staff on the following afternoon. Within less than two weeks, all the patients had been transferred to other hospitals, or discharged, with appropriate plans made for their continuing treatment. On October 8, 1960, Crest formally ceased operations.

A news item in a Columbia newspaper noted that the president of the board stated: ". . . financial difficulties, which have plagued the non-profit hospital increasingly the past two years, forced the decision." The article continued:

"The community support for an organization such as Crest, which has aspired to the highest ideals of patient care, education and research never has been forthcoming," Dr. Thomas Doren, medical director, said. "It is hard to believe that this could happen, but perhaps some new effort can be forthcoming in the future to attempt to meet the needs of the mentally ill. One of the real tragedies is that there are so few places in the country to which we can send our patients for the type of care they have been receiving."

CHAPTER EIGHT

Legacy

What legacy is bequeathed us from Crest's ten years of active life? From its birth and death? Is there anything in this history that can provide guidelines for those involved with institutions now or in the future? Does the history support previous research and theorizing about groups, hospitals, and other institutions? Does it offer refinements of old ideas? More than that, what is new, what fresh insights are contributed to persistent problems?

The conclusions of this study will be presented on two levels, the practical and the theoretical. Such a division is useful for analytic reasons, but these levels cannot really be separated. Clearly, the theoretical level is more important: the rationale for generalizing from one instance to another is the essence of theory. But what can be learned from one instance that is applicable to other instances is a practical as well as a theoretical problem. The first part of this chapter contains practical conclusions. The theoretical, social scientific analysis, from which the practical suggestions stem, is offered in the following, final section.

The practical conclusions are not to be considered rules for running a hospital or a similar institution. No such rules can be formulated. But people in institutions may be blind to some of the results of their actions. The effects cited in the following discussion do not always take place; additional factors may cancel, modify, and distort the instances presented. Moreover, it is not possible to make accurate and valid judgments about the relative importance of various facets of the history of Crest. Even if such judgments could be made, the relative values would not obtain for other institutions, however much they may resemble Crest.

Certain types of effects, however, can and often occur. In describing how actions of involved people can influence the viability of an institution, illustrations of influences on the degree of hope are emphasized. That is, how did the actions of people involved with Crest affect the level of excitement and enthusiasm in its early history? How did their behavior contribute to the decline of enthusiasm in Crest's last years?

Although Crest was an aspiring institution, the processes which helped to maintain it are the same—differing only in intensity—as those which serve to maintain an institution simply as an institution, at any level of excitement. Underlying this generality of application is the fact that all types of institutions, ambitious or not, inevitably encounter threats to their existence or to their optimism. The ways in which threats are overcome are basically the same, but all of the ways are not necessary for all institutions. Methods can substitute for or enhance one another; or, one process may be very strong and make up for the absence of others. There are no fixed rules.

Legacy: Practical Implications

The practical conclusions are organized around a series of social roles, including the lay community, the professional community, the Board of Trustees, and the medical director.

The Lay Community

The decline and demise of Crest were the results, in part, of its lack of a solid base in the lay community. The viability and excitement of any institution are enhanced by active support—financial, moral, and in other ways—from people who adhere to its basic philosophy or ideology. Lay supporters do not need to comprehend fully all the details of the ideology. However, affirmation of the essence of the ideology permits the contribution by individuals of time, energy, and money, even in the face of frustration and shocks. Furthermore, knowledge of an involvement with the ideology better equips them to make choices consistent with it in the rare but crucial instances they are called on to do so. These instances occur when the lay supporters receive no professional guidance in making policy decisions, or have to choose between disagreeing experts.

The responsibility for educating the lay supporters rests with the professionals, primarily with those who run the organization—in this case the hospital. One basic problem is the amount of time and energy that the professionals and the lay members are willing and able to devote to education. Both groups have other commitments and interests. It is important, therefore, that supporters begin with a sympathy for the ideology.

The Crest board members were enthusiastic, dedicated, and supportive, but the professional people recognized that they failed to communicate successfully to the board the ideas they wished to see prevail at the hospital. Dr. Clark observed that ". . . the board was never indoctrinated [professionally] and taught; they never learned anything, really." Another psychiatrist adds, in the beginning "[we had]a concept in mind which we believed in and which we were not able to transmit to those who were furnishing the money. I think it seemed to them at times as if we were dictating to them, whereas here they were furnishing the money, and the person who furnishes the money really has the say." Board members, although they resented the feeling of being "dictated to," had no well-developed ideas of their own, so that a psychiatrist notes, ". . . when the professional people let down, well then the lay people were . . . never really able to pick it up and know what to do with this hospital . . . how to run it or what attitude to have."

A second, related lesson from the history of Crest is that the financial supporters of the hospital should not be in a position in which they can exercise their power maximally. Inevitably, the contributors will exercise influence, but it is clear that a high degree of influence can have negative results, especially if disagreement exists between the professionals running the hospital and the donors. That is, if there is not ideological agreement, the exercise of financial power becomes increasingly important. Money from members of the lay community should be given free and clear, with no contingencies attached. Another way to minimize the exercise of power based on finances would be to enlist advocates from a wide variety of sources in the community. Taking or accepting support from only one person or group makes a hospital especially vulnerable to any exercise of power by that person or group. Crest's financial support was, unfortunately, limited to a very small group.

A third lesson is that the financial backers should be told that during a special need or crisis they must be prepared to give the hospital more funds than they are usually responsible for raising. Since they are responsible for the financial stability of the institution, they must be made to realize that there will be times when additional money is needed. The difficulties of the Board of Trustees in the last years of Crest, and their discomfort in defining fund-raising as their function, point up the need to prepare the way in advance.

Professional-Community Relationships

The vulnerability of Crest to controversy among Columbia psychiatrists is painfully evident in its history. Crest originally was sponsored by a part of the local professional community. For a while, their support was sufficient to sustain the hospital. But when this group divided and changed its character, support for the hospital diminished. It does not follow that professional support should have been broadly based to begin with; the hospital would have had to be eclectic and compromising in its ideology. Such eclecticism could not have inspired the kind of dedication present at Crest during its early years. However, some way must be found to assure the continued support of the group of professionals who are behind the governing ideology.

The best solution to this complex problem appears to be that professional endorsement should come from people of one point of view. Both trustees and hospital staff at times turn to outside professionals for guidance and help. When the professionals are

united, the kind of dedication that strengthens a hospital is facilitated. The omission of part of the professional community
makes the "in-group" more tightly knit, and enhances the degree of agreement. Division among the professionals who support
the hospital confuses the lay supporters and the hospital staff and
forces lay trustees to arbitrate among the conflicting professionals. Such a responsibility is not one for which they are suited
by training or motivation.

A second lesson follows from the first. Relationships between
the professional and lay groups should be so structured as to
minimize the opportunities for the lay trustees to be caught in
the middle of a conflict. Conflict situations of this sort were
common in Crest's history, but it is doubtful that any similar
organization can escape some amount of similar conflict. When
professionals are members of the Board of Trustees, conflict is
facilitated because professional trustees are put in the position of
having divided loyalties. Furthermore, the trustees should not be
in a position to "choose" the leader of the professional group,
as they did with Crawford, or to remove one, as they did when
Dr. Clark represented the consultant staff. Some conflicts cannot
be avoided by the board—for example, the division between Drs.
Crawford and Clark. But the organization of the professional
community and its relationship with the board should be designed to minimize the consequences of such conflicts.

The effects of interprofessional conflict might be reduced by
having the professionals organized separately from the board, so
that they can present a single professional point of view. Conflicts and difficulties then would be resolved or contained within
the professional group, although not necessarily extinguished.

A third lesson concerns the attitude and behavior of the professionals toward the hospital. Their behavior should indicate
respect for the integrity and autonomy of the hospital. However,
this is sometimes difficult to maintain. The professional community may take a "parental" attitude toward the hospital, as
Drs. Clark and Crawford sometimes did. Development of the
hospital may be seen as an economic threat by parts of the local
professional community. The community psychiatrists may view
the hospital as being of low status as a consequence, for ex-

ample, of the relatively low status of the hospital director, e.g., Dr. Dale; or their attitude may develop from the psychiatric tendency to view as a patient the organization which they are helping, as the committee of consultants did in Crest's last years.

Board of Trustees

Many of the points already set forth have implications for the Board of Trustees; there are, however, other problems that concern them directly. First, there should be a high consensus among all the people involved in the running of a hospital concerning the role of the Board of Trustees. As has been described, many consultants and hospital staff members, as well as some board members, did not know that the board was not fully committed to the role of raising money, nor did they know that doubt and equivocation as to this function had occurred when the board was established, and later when new board members were being sought. Bitterness, therefore, developed as a result of the board's failure to raise money; it was assumed that that was their prime responsibility.

In a hospital the board is also faced with dealing with data, facts, and information relating to clinical functioning. How much knowledge of the professional area do they require to function effectively? How much need they know of the difficulties in the day-to-day operation of a hospital? Should they be informed only of the hospital's successes? Should they limit themselves to a concern with finances, public relations, and such matters? These problems arise only when something important goes awry. The gravity of the problems engendered when things do go wrong in a hospital is illustrated by two examples from Crest's history. In one, the board was sharply informed of actual difficulties: Dr. Clark blatantly denounced Dr. Dunn to the trustees. In the second instance, difficulties were not communicated: Dr. Doren did not immediately inform the trustees of the epidemic of suicides. Neither course of action was adequate; the trustees could not deal effectively with the problems.

One must assume that a mental hospital, or any institution, will regularly encounter difficulties. Patient behavior, for example, is subject to more influences than the hospital can control—acute upsets are bound to occur. The staff, too, are not immune to upsets stemming from sources outside the hospital; personal problems affect the clinical performance of therapeutic personnel. The Board of Trustees, then, must be prepared for difficulties; they cannot be kept uninformed. It is imperative that the trustees' basic belief in the ideology of the hospital should not be shaken by their knowledge of necessary difficulties. Some trustees may need to know much about the general field, for example, psychiatry, before they can accept difficulties as inevitable and passing. Others may prefer to know very little. The amount of knowledge is less important than the way the knowledge influences acceptance of difficulties without loss of dedication. Board members can learn the same attitudes as professionals without extensive training and knowledge. Therapeutic procedures should be seen working to raise the probability of successful treatment; all patients will not be "cured." To be sure, a great deal of enthusiasm for a given form of therapy can be generated among professionals, as in the early days of Crest. But such enthusiasm exists within a context of probabilities. "Crest could cure anyone," described a belief in the possibility, but not an expectation of one hundred per cent success.

The trustees, while being aware of the possibilities of trouble, should be cognizant of the possibilities of solution of possible difficulties. They should not cut themselves off from sources of potential support, even though this support may not be necessary at the time. They should make continual efforts to keep in close contact with the consultants, and with sources of money in the community. They should, in a sense, keep their fences mended at all times.

Clearly some members of Crest's board were motivated to participate by past or present concerns with mental illness, either their own or friends' or relatives' experiences. Many of the trustees would not have become involved without these personal factors, nor would their dedication have been so great. Sometimes such motivation seemed to underlie serious distortions of judgment about the hospital. At other times this source of motivation enhanced involvement. In sum, such personal involvements do not necessarily have unhappy consequences, and the advantages should not be underestimated.

Medical Directorship

The discussion of the lay and professional communities has been directly relevant to the problems of the medical directorship. It is helpful for the director to have the respect of the professional community, both in terms of his ideas and his professional rank and stature. It is useful in educating the lay Board of Trustees, a task logically falling on the medical director. And, it is important that the independence and autonomy of a hospital be respected, which in large measure is a consequence of the respect awarded the independence and autonomy of the medical director.

The medical director is the focus of many processes vital to the functioning of an institution such as Crest. He has to believe completely in the institution and must be able to impart the depth and strength of his conviction to the hospital staff and to the professional community. The director, too, should emphasize respect for the hospital staff's autonomy and integrity. This does not mean that he should abandon the staff, but that he should give guidance and leadership in a way that communicates respect. For example, Drs. Dunn and Davidson, in different ways, delegated much of the responsibility for the day-to-day clinical work, yet were able to give over-all guidance to the hospital staff.

One way of communicating basic belief in the hospital is to expand and develop it in plant, staff, or refinements of treatment methods. Growth communicates dramatically and tangibly, while not undermining the integrity of the staff. The director can become a leader facing out into the community, drawing from it new support, new ideas, new people; in that way he does not have to "face in" to the staff in any way that threatens their integrity. Although it was not always a major factor in Crest, this process is exemplified by Dr. Davidson's plans for the hospital and his increasing tendency to consider the beliefs and feelings of the staff in his administrative decisions. Dunn behaved in a similar manner. On the other hand, Dr. Dale "faced in"; he was most concerned with administrative problems.

One implication of this discussion is that it is less important to have a medical director who possesses a high degree of clinical ability than to have one who has the leadership traits described above. During the final years of Crest's existence, some of the professionals were convinced that the medical director need only be a highly qualified psychoanalyst; the abilities cited above are not necessarily correlated with stature as a psychoanalyst. In the Crest situation, the analytic status of the medical directors was not a crucial factor in their relationship with the professional community; all the directors suffered similar fates. Yet, as stated earlier, the professional stature of the director can be necessary to gain the respect and cooperation of his colleagues. The job of medical director is a conglomerate of different roles, each requiring that a different asset be most salient. Thus, for the outside professional group, the director must have high professional stature; for the hospital, he must be a good leader; the board, at times, wished him to be a good salesman. In Crest's history, none of the directors fulfilled all the demands of the position.

The suggestions above are some—by no means all—of the practical implications of the Crest story. They stem from the general, social scientific analysis—which follows immediately— and which can be a source for many additional practical leads and guides.

Legacy: Theoretical Analysis

In this section implications of the Crest history are related to broader conceptions of social psychology and sociology. A rationale is provided for many practical propositions, as well as to indicate some of the ways in which the findings of the study are consistent with or different from other data and general theorizing. The theoretical analysis does not follow from any single system, nor are the richness and complexity of the material ignored. In examining a history such as that of Crest, many facets may legitimately be chosen for scientific examination, and each may be examined from many viewpoints and levels. The basic level of analysis is the institution; however, social psychological ideas and data about interactions among people and their motivations and perceptions are included, in order better to understand the processes observed at the institutional level. At times, in fact, the analysis rests at the social psychological, interpersonal level.

Crest was a hospital for people with severe emotional disturbance. Essential to the following theoretical considerations is the conviction that hope is a necessary if not sufficient condition for the successful treatment of mental patients. Jerome D. Frank, in his discussion of psychodynamic aspects of the psychotherapeutic relationship, states that certain properties are characteristic of all therapeutic relationships. He notes that in all therapies, "the therapist inevitably exerts a strong influence on the patient. This influence arises primarily from the patient's hope or faith that treatment will relieve his distress."[1] Such influence is in part determined by the therapist's confidence in his ability to help the patient. The therapist's potential influence on patients depends as well on the patient's expectations that the therapy will be helpful. This expectation often is a consequence of desperation, which, in turn, leads the patient to be more dependent and suggestible. Ambiguity and increased anxiety also lead in the same direction; the patient is then more dependent on the feeling he picks up from the therapist—more needful of help, and, in this sense, more urgently hopeful about the only source of help, the therapist. One can anticipate, as Frank does, the complaint of some clinicians that the therapeutic effects of such hope and faith can be only superficial; that long-term treatment, insight into the individual's basic problems, and "working through," are necessary, if treatment is to be of lasting value. But substantial evidence supporting such a point of view is absent.

There is much data that strongly suggest that the patient's expectations, his hopefulness—often engendered by the therapist

[1] Jerome D. Frank, "Dynamics of the Psychotherapeutic Relationship," *Psychiatry*, XXII (1959), 17–41. Also, Jerome D. Frank, *Persuasion and Healing* (Baltimore, Md.: The Johns Hopkins Press, 1961).

—are powerful factors in therapy, and that short-term therapy may be as effective as long-term treatment.[2,3] Our intensive study of the suicide epidemic at Crest shows clearly that the loss of hope in the atmosphere at Crest was a necessary condition for the patients to commit suicide.[4] Other studies of emotional disturbances among patients in mental hospitals[5] can be interpreted in terms of the patients' loss of hope. Upsets among patients following communicational and other difficulties among staff can be seen as a consequence of the reduced self-confidence, the decline in hopefulness of expectations, among the staff members. Their discouragement was communicated to the patients in a variety of ways. It was the absence of hope, from our point of view, that led to increased anxiety, collective outbreaks of pathological excitement, and general deterioration of patient behavior.

The significance for the patient of the hopefulness of the therapist and therapeutic personnel points up the importance of studying the factors determining the expections of the hospital staff members about patients. Hospital personnel who deal directly with patients are vulnerable to loss of hope about the patients, to loss of commitment to therapeutic objectives, and to loss of confidence in their own attainment. When daily contacts with patients are the only basis for supporting the staff's high expectations, sooner or later some seemingly insurmountable difficulty with a patient or a group of patients will occur. It is essential to understand the processes by which the hopefulness of the staff can be maintained in the face of inevitable difficulties. These processes are a major focus of the present study, and their examination is an essential part of its *raison d'être*.

[2] Arnold Goldstein, *Patient-Therapist Expectations in Psychotherapy* (New York: Macmillan and Co., 1962).

[3] For the importance of hope in therapy, see also Thomas M. French, *The Integration of Behavior*, Vol. I. (Chicago: University of Chicago Press, 1952); and Karl Menninger, *The Vital Balance* (New York: The Viking Press, 1963).

[4] Kobler and Stotland, *The End of Hope.*

[5] Alfred H. Stanton and Morris S. Schwartz, *The Mental Hospital* (New York: Basic Books, 1954); and William Caudill, *The Psychiatric Hospital as a Small Society* (Cambridge, Mass.: Harvard University Press, 1958).

Hope and Immediate Reality

What are the factors that maintain or destroy hopefulness for staff members of an institution? How can hope be sustained when the events of everyday life do not support it? How can one face a bleak reality directly and still be hopeful? These questions can be seen as instances of a broader problem, that of being "realistic." Too often great value is placed on "facing facts," and being realistic is often equated with being mature, as an attribute of adjustment and mental health. It is also propounded as a criteria of the sound functioning of organizations of all sorts, such as businesses, schools, armies, and foundations. The problem of potential conflict between hopefulness and realism is not confined to the running of a mental hospital; it is a general concern for all types of groups as well as for individuals. All face difficulties in the achievement of goals and objectives, and all must be able to withstand the challenge of disagreeable facts.

The problem of how to maintain hope will be dealt with from several standpoints: from the point of view of Crest, of other mental hospitals like Crest, and of other groups and institutions. One implication of this approach is highlighted by the emphasis in some sociological thinking which regards the development of the social processes among members of groups as a derivative or function of the environmental pressures on the group.[6] In these terms, the internal structure of a group, the pattern and content of interactions, are most heavily influenced by the external system, or the way the group relates to its environment. The way that groups function is assumed to be a function of the "facts." If the facts are discouraging, it is assumed that there will be some deterioration in a group's effort to achieve its goals; a hopelessness will rise.

But hopelessness is not at all a necessary outcome of frustration. One can see the internal formal structure of the group itself as a source of hopefulness, as the group attempts to achieve its goals. That is, the group's reactions to the environment, and

[6] Robert F. Bales, *Interaction Process Analysis: A Method for the Study of Small Groups* (Cambridge, Mass.: Addison Wesley Publishing Co., 1950); George C. Homans, *The Human Group* (New York: Harcourt, Brace and Co., 1950).

most especially to failure to achieve goals in the external environment, may be a function of the internal system. Perceptual variables, the way in which the members of a group perceive and construe the environment, are emphasized in this frame of reference, rather than the "objective" characteristics of the environment.

In beginning the consideration of the sources of hope which operate in the face of a sometimes harsh reality, aspects of the story of Crest are pertinent. One pervasive fact at Crest is that the patients were upset, anxious, and bizarre in thought and behavior. Yet the staff and other involved people were not often overwhelmed; generally they maintained their eagerness. The enthusiasm of the founders for Crest as a psychoanalytically and milieu-oriented hospital was not based on a substantial body of scientifically validated evidence. Nor was the intense involvement of the early directors founded on "data." The early therapeutic practices at Crest differed little from those of other hospitals, yet people felt that the treatment was uniquely effective. In the beginning, the ward staff believed in the special signifiance of attitude therapy; yet there was no evidence to support their belief. The board, too, trusted in the effectiveness of the hospital. How could faith be maintained so long without supportive facts?

What is the nature of the "facts" about the difficulties of helping mental hospital patients? The painfully raw data of a patient's behavior may include, at a given moment, terror, hallucinations, delusions, or depression. The reactions of people around him are not simply a reaction to his behavior, except at rare times. Reactions usually are governed by what is perceived to be the meaning of the behavior, the implications that the patient's behavior has for his feelings and behavior in the future. A patient's terror may be interpreted as indicating that he is "facing his problems," and will therefore get well. Delusional thinking may be viewed as a defensive reaction that bodes well, or poorly, for the patient. The importance of interpreting what a bit of a patient's behavior implies for the future is sharply exemplified by such a notion as "flight into health." The patient suddenly begins to act in a "healthy" way; his symptoms vanish. The therapist may view this change as an improvement, or as indicating that the patient's problem will soon overwhelm him in an even more devastating fashion.[7]

Although therapeutic institutions are explicity oriented to change and to the future, reactions to patients in terms of implications for the future are but one instance of the general human tendency to respond to other people's behavior in terms of its meaning for future behavior, rather than in terms of the behavior itself.[8] It has been demonstrated that every bit of a person's behavior implies a great deal about his behavior, thoughts, and feelings.[9] We react to these implications; but they are not grounded in facts about the other person. Rather, they appear to be based on "implicit theories of personality," theories about human behavior held by ordinary people who rarely are able to articulate them.[10] People go beyond facts to the future. They need to make decisions about their own future behavior, their own commitments and plans of action. They need clarity and stability in their picture of the future.

A person's reactions, then, to mental patients are not different from his reactions in more common situations. But, if the reactions are based on an interpretation of others' behavior, what are the bases for hopeful interpretations? Neither psychoanalysis, experimental psychology, nor literature has reached the state of certainty that can provide a sure basis for predicting people's

[7] See, in this connection, Kobler and Stotland, *The End of Hope*, concerning the expectations of "suicidal" patients who improve.

[8] George H. Mead, *Mind, Self and Society* (Chicago: University of Chicago Press, 1934). Mead distinguishes, perhaps too sharply, between human and animal behavior, in that humans react in terms of the future implications of an act, while animals do not.

[9] Solomon Asch, *Social Psychology* (Englewood Cliffs, N.J.: Prentice-Hall, Inc., 1952) ; Fritz Heider, *The Psychology of Interpersonal Relations* (New York: John Wiley and Sons, 1958) ; Harold H. Kelley, "The Warm-Cold Variable in First Impressions of Persons," *Journal of Personality*, XVIII (1950), 431–39; Abraham Luchins, "Primacy-Recency in Impression Formation," in *The Order of Presentation in Persuasion*, Vol. I, ed. Carl I. Hovland (New Haven, Conn.: Yale University Press, 1957).

[10] Jerome S. Bruner, David Shapiro, and Renato Taguiri, "The Meaning of Traits in Isolation and in Combination," in *Person Perception and Interpersonal Behavior*, eds. Renato Taguiri and Luigi Pettrallo (Stanford, Calif.: Stanford University Press, 1958).

future behavior. More particularly, the use of any source as a possible base for hopeful interpretations of the behavior of patients suffers from the serious limitation that no single criterion of cure has been agreed upon. Studies on the meaning of "adjustment" have revealed a variety of criteria; lack of anxiety, social effectiveness, accurate perception of oneself and the world, absence of symptoms, and many more.[11] At different times and by different people, these and other criteria are given different weights. For a psychoanalyst, accurate perception of the self may be most important. For a head of a family, social effectiveness may be most pertinent. Furthermore, each of these criteria, taken separately, cannot, in most cases, be definitively applied. When is social effectiveness adequately effective? How deep does insight have to be? In fact, how does one measure social effectiveness and depth of insight in the first place? Furthermore these criteria contradict one another. A man's symptoms may return every time he takes on responsibility. A very anxious person may have great insight into his problems. There is little question then that the goals of mental health institutions lack "operationability";[12] that is, one cannot ascertain empirically how well the organization is attaining its goals. Goals in the mental health field are too diverse, too diffuse, too potentially contradictory to be easily operationable.[13] In short, workers in the field of mental health are faced with a difficult situation. The facts that they encounter regularly can easily be interpreted in a negative fashion, yet a positive interpretation is necessary for their effectiveness in achieving their goals.

If there are no unequivocal data, what remains, then, is a set of beliefs, of convictions, a faith, an ideology. The beliefs that people have about others remain at the level of "theory," a theory relative to their goals and means of attaining them. Since support for such theories cannot come from immediate "facts," it

[11] William A. Scott, "Research Definitions of Mental Health and Mental Illness," *Psychological Bulletin*, LVIII (1958), 29–45.

[12] James G. March and Herbert A. Simon, *Organizations* (New York: John Wiley and Sons, 1958).

[13] It may be that in many other organizations that are pioneering new areas, the goals are unoperational; that only in well-established areas are the goals operational.

must come from other sources. At Crest, in the early years, there was much hope about helping patients. An ideology developed that Crest could cure anyone, including those who had been given up as failures and were considered hopeless by other hospitals and therapists. No matter how badly off a patient might appear, no matter how deteriorated his behavior, he was thought of as helpable. The ideology functioned as a buffer, so that difficulties in treating patients did not cause the staff to give up. The potential conflict between "reality" and "hopefulness" was not a problem. The sources of such a hopeful ideology are in large part social, deriving from other people and groups. They should not be vulnerable to discouragement, shock, or disillusionment from day to day difficulties of dealing with patients. The ideology can be supported without too much concern for the facts of difficulties if the sources of the ideology are not directly affected by difficulties.

The analysis of the sources of the hopeful ideology of Crest is pertinent to all sorts of institutions or groups which do not have clear, objective ways of making the degree of achievement of goals operational, such as religious or educational groups, who cannot be certain about how their moral or ethical values are applied by their "clients." The analysis is also meaningful to groups which have to face "facts" which raise serious questions about their effectiveness in achieving their goals. These include mental hospitals where discouraging outcomes in the treatment of some patients always occur, as well as "correctional" institutions, military groups, and some businesses. Of course, if the disheartening instances are clear, frequent, and important to the personnel of the organization, none of the sources of the strength of the ideology may be able to sustain hope. This occurred increasingly in the last years of Crest; the adolescent rebellion and the epidemic of suicides were devastating to most dedicated Crestites.

Hopefulness, and supports and sources of hope, are more significant for groups that are exciting, new, dynamic, and that are attempting to achieve difficult goals. Such groups are more likely to encounter facts that could easily be interpreted negatively. They are also more likely to work toward goals that are not

highly operational, since their goals are new and have not
been attained in the past. These are not the only groups that
have problems of nonoperability of goals, or that must face
facts which are readily interpreted in a hopeless manner. Few
institutions have not faced crises, or have not on occasion been
without firm guidelines. The sources of hopefulness apply to all
institutions, but are more pertinent for groups which aspire to
more.[14]

Before describing, and discussing in detail, sources of a hopeful ideology, it should be noted that the sources are substitutible.
If one source is not applicable, another may function to maintain
the strength of the institution. For example, if the official leadership of an institution fails, a group of experts might function to
legitimize the institution. Also, each source is not equally effective; and, finally, the sources might contradict one another and
function at cross purposes with regard to the institution's ideology.

Sources of the Hopefulness of Ideologies

First of all, the ideology of Crest derived from its parent institution, the Menninger Foundation. The founders of the hospital and the early staff leaders all came from Menningers. During the years that they were at Topeka, Menningers was an
especially exciting and pioneering institution. The founders of
Crest had a strong conviction that psychoanalytically oriented
psychotherapy and milieu therapy, as practiced at Menningers,
was the most effective treatment program for hospitalized mental
patients. They received encouragement from Topeka for their
new enterprise. They thus acquired a reflected charisma from the
internationally known and highly reputed Menninger name.

The process of one institution endowing another with an

[14] A question arises as to the consequences of a loss of hopefulness in an
institution with a high level of aspiration. Does it retract to a lower level?
Does it become defunct? The first question should not be glibly resolved by
simply defining the organization with the fallen level of aspiration as a
"different" organization from the original one. The answer probably would
depend on such factors as the number of other goals the organization and
its members have that can be satisfied by it; or the degree to which the
institution can do with half a loaf. We only raise this problem here and
suggest possible answers.

ideology is not simply an intellectual educational process, but a motivational and emotional one. An individual believes that an institution has the right ideology because it has been derived from an omnipotent parent institution. The process of endowing someone with charisma, as Weber[15] described it, is not limited to an interpersonal process; it can also occur between groups and institutions. Charisma can be transferred between institutions in a number of ways: by recruitment of personnel; by adoption of the same ideology; by a transfer of the enthusiasm of pioneers. The significance of this reflected charisma was greatest at the beginning of Crest, even before its actual opening. At this stage, participants have the least amount of support for their ideology from other sources; their belief in the effectiveness of the hospital hinges on reflected glory. (Perhaps this is a general phenomenon; it may be that early in the history of many institutions hopefulness of ideology is a consequence of reflected charisma.)

Crest was not close to Menningers. Distance from the parent institution is helpful; separation provides a safeguard against close contact with the unavoidable difficulties of the parent institution. Distantly, the parent's image can remain aglow; the Menningerites on the Crest staff retained their positive picture. Findings in experimental psychology speak to the importance of distance with regard to "goal gradients"; the farther one is from a goal, the more likely one is to respond to positive rather than negative aspects of the goal. Assuming that the goal gradient phenomenon is more general, distance from Menningers made it a more effective source of strength.

A second source of the strength of the ideology is the support that an institution receives from other institutions, groups, or persons who are not expert in the function of the institution. The essence of the support of such groups is their power or high status position in other areas. Their value may be both practical and symbolic. The help communicates confidence and support from important, powerful people and groups. These supports, because of their nonexpertness and noninvolvement in the day-to-day functioning of the institution, are less vulnerable to the

---

[15] Max Weber, *A Theory of Social and Economic Organization* (New York: Oxford University Press, 1947).

discouraging or ambiguous "facts" that confront the more involved people. The continued support of these lay, outside groups helps those who are directly involved to remain hopeful in the face of difficulties. In institutions with ties to larger organizations, the source of outside support may not be a lay group, but an expert group not vulnerable to immediate difficulties. Thus, practical or even symbolic support from the "national" may be sufficient to tide the "local" over a difficulty.

At Crest, this type of support was illustrated in the ways in which the hospital was supported by lay members of the Board of Trustees. The speed with which money for opening the hospital was contributed fed the enthusiasm of the founders. The status in the community of some of the members of the board was not unnoticed by the people at the hospital. In the last years of Crest, the hospital staff expected the board to raise the needed money. When the board failed, staff members felt let down by the community. Thus, this source of support is only useful to an organization when it is effective, viable, and hopeful itself.

A third source of support for the ideology of an institution is groups of experts outside of the institution. Members of the institution can derive support for its ideology from these experts. The Crest trustees, and, to some degree, the hospital staff, were influenced by the degree of confidence in Crest of professionals in Columbia and in other parts of the country. The power of this influence became apparent and significant when the director proved inadequate to cope with difficulties that arose at the hospital. The board, having no objective criterion of the effectiveness of the hospital, was then dependent on the expert opinion of the professional community. In the early days of Crest, the board received approbation from most of the local psychiatric community; certainly there was no active, organized derogation. Its perception of general support was enhanced by Crest's quickly developing national reputation, and the increasing rate of referrals, both from the local community and from the nation at large.

These factors of expert support are important in other hospitals, and other kinds of institutions, as well as at Crest. It was found that in two equally wealthy communities the better hos-

pitals had received continued support from experts in and outside the community, i.e., the state university's medical school, the
federal government, the local medical association. The directors
of the hospital were impressed by the continued support of the
hospital by these experts, and were exceedingly proud when they
received a special accolade from them.[16]

It is clearly valuable for an institution to be "legitimized" by a
relevant group of experts.[17] Talcott Parsons speaks of the legitimization of the hospital in the community:

> The relevant mechanisms concern the ensuring of com-
> munity "confidence" in the hospital. This will include
> the "community standing," the reputation for responsi-
> bility of the elements in the community who sponsor the
> hospital and take responsibility for the integrity and
> technical competence of its administration. It will also
> include the utilization of the relevant professional
> groups, particularly the medical profession, not simply in
> a technological sense, but as guarantors of the bona fide
> character of the operation. The formula in general is that
> if reputable medical personnel associate themselves with
> the hospital it must be "all right." More specifically,
> these processes include the diffuse area of "public rela-
> tions," the mechanisms by which the "right" of the or-
> ganization to operate and the appeal to give it support
> are established.

However, some of the factors which make an institution dependent on such legitimization make the legitimization itself
vulnerable. The institution is dependent upon outside experts
when, lacking leadership, clear facts are unavailable for the "operationability" of the goals, or the available facts are "discouraging." But the lack of such clear or encouraging facts makes the
support from experts a subjective matter; it is a matter of the

[16] Ivan Belknap and John G. Steinle, *The Community and Its Hospitals:
A Comparative Analysis* (Syracuse, N.Y.: Syracuse University Press, 1963).

[17] Talcott Parsons, "The Mental Hospital as a Type of Organization," in
The Patient and the Mental Hospital, eds. Morris Greenblatt, Daniel J.
Levinson, and Robert H. Williams (Glencoe, Ill.: The Free Press, 1957),
p. 113.

ideology of the experts themselves. The strength of their ideology is, in part, a function of the degree of agreement among the experts. Agreement may be subject to changes, shifts, and redefinition, because of factors having little to do with the content of the ideology, such as personality conflicts, power struggles, competitiveness, and changing composition and needs of the expert group. At Crest, the results of changes within the psychiatric community were unpredictable. The split between Crawford and Clark arose from factors having nothing directly to do with Crest, but it had vast consequences for the hospital. The effect of conflict between groups of experts is exacerbated if the opposed groups are officially separated. Dr. Crawford's membership on the Board of Trustees meant that the lay members were faced with two sets of experts, those on and off the board.

On the other hand there are forces within the expert group working to maintain a high degree of agreement. Social psychological findings show that groups apply strong pressures on deviant members to conform to the judgments made by the group.[18] Maintaining agreement helps individual members feel certain of their beliefs, and adhere to the ideology. When a deviant member resists pressures to adhere to the group, he is in danger of rejection.[19] At Crest the nonpsychoanalytically oriented psychiatrists were ejected from the hospital. To be sure, part of this rejection stemmed from the practical problem of running a hospital in a consistent fashion; but it was also motivated by the need to have a high degree of agreement among members of the group.

A fourth source of support for the ideology of a group or institution is "facts," empirical data which are construed as evidence for, or symbols of, the effectiveness of the institution or group.[20] These facts are available, and have varying degrees of equivocality. While they do not provide direct evidence, they can be interpreted as being indicative of the achievement of

[18] Leon Festinger, "Informal Social Communication," *Psychological Review*, LVII (1950), 271–82.

[19] Stanley Schachter, "Deviation, Rejection and Communication," *Journal of Abnormal and Social Psychology*, XLVII (1951), 190–207.

[20] March and Simon, *Organizations*.

goals. At Crest such facts included: growth of the physical plant; recruitment of new, highly qualified staff members; growing financial strength; and a high patient census. When, in later years, these signs became negative, the morale of the hospital staff and trustees declined. The leveling-off of the rate of expansion of the physical plant; the uncompleted building on the grounds; the drop in the census; the failure to replace the residents and other professionals; the financial difficulties; the strange series of illnesses and deaths among staff, ex-staff, and ex-patients in the months following the adolescent rebellion; the difficulty in finding a new director; all of these were taken as signs of deterioration of the hospital.

Some of the facts, such as the size and quality of the professional staff, probably are related to the actual effectiveness of the hospital. Others, such as the rate of expansion of the physical plant, are less clearly related. The degree of influence these factors have is the result of such items as the clarity of the facts, their availability, and the way in which they fit into the frame of reference of the people involved. For example, the trustees tended to emphasize two facts in their evaluation of the hospital's effectiveness: its financial status and the patient census. Both of these were clear and available; furthermore, they fit into the usual ways of thinking of the trustees, most of whom were businessmen. These facts may be an index of the effectiveness of the hospital. For example, a high census can be a function of a high rate of referrals indicating confidence in the hospital. But the census and financial state are also influenced by the speed of recovery of the patients; the criterion for recovery used; the length of stay seen as necessary for recovery, however defined; the criteria used to screen patients; the rate of growth of the hospital; the collection of accounts receivable; and the size of competitive institutions. It is difficult, if not impossible, to define the factors affecting the census and financial status of the hospital at different times, yet they were constantly referred to and interpreted.

For a variety of institutions and groups, signs of growth may be effective in instilling confidence and hopefulness. An institution which has "projects," and which continues to grow steadily, may find such growth a support for its ideology, independent of the degree to which the growth actually enhances the effectiveness of the institution. On the other hand, there are pitfalls in this process. A history of expansion of an institution may raise the aspiration of staff members to an unreasonable level. Studies indicate that groups tend to set their level of aspiration at a point slightly above their previous level of performance.[21] The staff may make itself vulnerable to disappointment *by setting itself the level of aspiration for a rate of change,* expecting change and growth at an accelerated rate. Some of the decline in enthusiasm among the staff in Crest's last years may have been due to this factor.[22] On the other hand, in some institutions physical growth and expansion of the staff might not be regarded as desirable and therefore would not be a source of hopefulness; the ideology might entail the institution's remaining small. Some people at Crest felt that to maintain its identity the hospital should not expand beyond thirty or at the most, fifty beds. Everybody agreed, however, that the physical plant needed improvement.

The history of an institution provides a kind of incontrovertible fact upon which the ideology can be based. The fact of its survival indicates that difficulties can be overcome. Thus, in the last years of Crest, many old-timers believed that Crest would solve its problems and return to its former glory. If Crest had had a longer history in the community, this fact alone might have led members of the local lay and professional communities to place more confidence in its continued existence. Others have described short-term cycles of disturbance in mental hospitals, caused by administrative changes, the departure of a key patient, the admission of a disturbing one, and others.[23] But the hospital staffs recognized these troubles as limited and solvable. The con-

[21] Alvin Zander and Herman Medow, "Individual and Group Levels of Aspiration," *Human Relations,* XVI (1963), 89–105.

[22] Mason Haire, "Biological Models and Empirical Histories in the Growth of Organizations," in *Modern Organization Theory,* ed. Mason Haire (New York: John Wiley and Sons, 1959).

[23] Caudill, *The Psychiatric Hospital;* Stanton and Schwartz, *The Mental Hospital;* David H. Rapoport, *Community as Doctor: New Perspectives in the Therapeutic Community* (London: Tavistock Publications, 1960).

tinued survival of many institutions in the face of present difficulties may depend on their longevity.

A fifth source of support for an ideology is the ideology itself. Some ideologies will satisfy the needs of the members of an organization more than others. Some beliefs enhance the self-esteem of the members of the group. This was true of the Crest ideology for the ward staff personnel. They were made important in the treatment process by the ideology of milieu and attitude therapy. Furthermore, the attitudes that they were to maintain toward the patients were not spelled out in detail; the ward personnel's sensitivity and resourcefulness were relied upon. They had to use judgment and initiative in working within the general framework of the prescribed behavior. This responsibility increased the attractiveness of the institution and its ideology for the ward staff; they were not only important, they also were responsible.[24] For the professionals, the emphasis on psychotherapy was important. This is high status work in the profession, "higher" than that usually done by hospital professionals.

Another characteristic of the Crest ideology that enhanced its acceptance by ward and professional personnel was that it was perceived as new and different in their region of the nation. The ideology was opposed by the adherents of other means of therapy, for example, those who emphasized physical methods. The perception of a threat from outside increases the cohesiveness of the group, and therefore strengthens a group's attachment to its ideology,[25] including its hopefulness. Thus, the staff members saw themselves as important people doing a unique job against opposition. Many ideologies have been accepted on this basis; for example, ideologies of new religious sects and of patriotic and

[24] In a variety of studies it has been found that workers are more satisfied if the amount of supervision they receive about details of a job is minimized. See Daniel Katz and Robert Kahn, "Leadership Practices in Relation to Productivity and Morale," in *Group Dynamics: Research and Theory*, eds. Dorwin Cartwright and Alvin Zander (Evanston, Ill.: Row-Peterson Co.: 1960).

[25] John Lanzetta, "Group Behavior Under Stress," *Human Relations*, VIII (1958), 29–52. Furthermore E. Wright Bakke has pointed out the great value to members of an organization of perceiving it as unique; this facilitates the members' identification with the institution and its ideology. Bakke, "Concept of Social Organization," in *Modern Organization Theory*.

nationalistic groups. If the ideology includes hopefulness, hope-fulness will receive additional support.

A sixth source of the strength of an ideology is the communi-cation processes within the group or institution. Communication in itself does not strengthen an ideology; some types of com-munication are strengthening, other types may have an opposite effect.[26] For example, the Crest hospital staff may have been upset by knowledge of the extent of Dr. Dunn's deterioration or of some of the more severe conflicts among the trustees and con-sultants. In these cases, communication was prevented by people who had access to the information; they may have been afraid of the consequences to the hospital staff of such knowledge, or they may not have considered the ward staff members as relevant per-sons to whom to communicate.

In many cases it is impossible to withhold communication about events which threaten the ideology or the institution; the events may be so obvious that they are known to all. Further-more, at times, anxiety may spread without any communication of content, of the facts upon which the affect is based.[27] The obviousness of threatening events and the general communi-cation of "contentless" affect is more likely to occur in small organizations such as Crest. In large institutions, the threat is generally limited to one department, so that the rest of the or-ganization can function as a stabilizer. It is necessary in small institutions to provide ways so that the members, receiving threatening communications, will not lose confidence in the ideology. First, in some cases the members can be told about the event by someone who is not anxious and who is in a position of knowlege or importance. Second, they can learn that action is planned or is being taken to resolve the problem. Third, they can be told of "new" aspects of the ideology which minimize the severity of the threat.[28]

---

[26] Stanton and Schwartz, *The Mental Hospital*, and Caudill, *The Psy-chiatric Hospital*, imply that communication per se is desirable in any organization. The emphasis in some studies of the negative effects of breakdown of communication gives the same impression.

[27] Caudill, *The Psychiatric Hospital*.

[28] Irving Janis has pointed out that people tend to react less maladjus-tively to disasters if they perceive that action is possible or is being taken

All of these methods were employed at Crest, especially in the early years. When there were difficulties with patients, and ward staff members felt inadequate, a meeting was called and the problems were discussed openly and directly. Measures to handle the situation and to prevent a recurrence were worked out; expectations about the ward staff's competence were positive; the future was faced with confidence, and the strength of the ideology was not reduced. In Crest's last year the staff was faced with the facts of a suicide attempt, followed by three actual suicides within a period of one month. A great deal of anxiety and fear-laden talk ensued, but no formal direct and constructive communication attempts were made. The continuing informal communication, then, fed a weakening of support of the institution.

A seventh source of support for the ideology of an institution is the educational processes within the organization. Such processes were elucidated by Etzioni,[29] who, in a comprehensive analytic study, divides complex organizations into three types in terms of the nature of the power which the organization or its representatives predominantly exercise over its members. One type of power is based on coercion, on fear of punishment for disobedience. Such organizations, for example, a prison, usually have goals of maintaining order. A second type of power is remunerative; the members obey because they receive some form of personal gain, material or otherwise, for doing so. Such organizations, for example, business establishments, often have economic goals. The third type of power is normative, in which members accept influence from the group because they feel a moral or ethical obligation to do so. The organization bases its appeal on the fact that its goals support or enhance the whole or part of the society within which the group functions. Normative groups are exemplified by religious groups, ideological organiza-

---

in the situation, that the "authorities" are competent and active. Janis, "Psychological Effects of Warnings," in *Man and Society in Disaster*, eds. George W. Baker and Dwight Chapman (New York: Basic Books, 1962).

[29] Amatai Etzioni, *A Comparative Analysis of Complex Organizations* (New York: The Free Press of Glencoe, 1961).

tions, colleges, voluntary organizations, and therapeutic mental hospitals.

Etzioni argues that the relationship between types of power and goals is functional and not accidental; that is, the exercise of the type of power is necessary for achievement of the organization's goals. For example, if a religious organization is to indoctrinate its laity, its clergy must believe in its righteousness. In fact, a concern over the beliefs of its clergy is characteristic of religious organizations. Neither paying the clergy to mouth an orthodoxy, nor threatening them if they fail to do so, would make them genuinely effective in or out of the pulpit.

Etzioni believes, along with others, that therapeutic mental hospitals like Crest must rely on the sense of obligation and dedication of its members for the achievement of its goals. This dependence is especially great if the ideology emphasizes milieu therapy, because all hospital personnel have to be involved. For them to adhere to the prescribed attitude out of fear of punishment would simply destroy the effectiveness of therapy. For one, it would not be feasible to check on the activities of all of the hospital personnel so as to detect and punish violators. And, in any case, the fear that would pervade the hospital staff would be communicated to the patients; the atmosphere would be antitherapeutic. For the hospital personnel to obey authority solely for remunerative reasons would be only slightly better. There would be less fear and hostility, but little involvement, dedication and hope. Thus, there is no other way that a therapeutic mental hospital, whose ideology includes milieu and attitude therapy, can be effective except by appealing to the sense of obligation of the members. They would then do their best under all circumstances, however unnoticed this was by the authorities. And their dedication would be obvious and beneficial to patients.

Etzioni points out that normative organizations typically emphasize the education or, as he calls it, secondary socialization, of new and old members, so that they accept and adhere to the norms or ideology of the institution. The importance for the ward staff to have a sense of involvement in the ideology was clear to the leaders of Crest, especially in the early years. The founders, the part-time medical directors, the first two full-time medical directors, all emphasized the importance of educating the ward staff, of communicating clearly and often with them, of listening to their problems and offering help. Throughout the early years of Crest, communication among all levels of personnel at the hospital was free and frequent. Only by means of this communication could the ideology of the hospital be established, and the hospital function as a normative organization.

The educative communication occurred not only from the top down, but also among persons of the same status within the hospital. In the early years of Crest, members of the ward staff educated new members, and continued to educate and support one another. This took place on the wards, and in the social groups that developed off the hospital grounds. The professional staff were also intensely close, at the hospital and socially. The education of people at all levels to the ideology of the hospital made communication easier and more effective. They shared a common frame of reference; informal communication among the levels was large in volume and importance for the personnel.

In short, the normative nature of the hospital required that all members be educated to the ideology; the effort to do so led to a general acceptance of the ideology, and, consequently, its hopefulness. In turn, the high level of acceptance both engendered and was supported by the high level of communication among the members of the hospital. People who think that others accept the same point of view will seek one another out, and their contacts will strengthen the conviction. If the accepted and supported ideology is a hopeful one, it receives additional support from within the institution; the group support and educative procedures within the organization all sustain hopefulness.

An eighth source of support for a hopeful ideology is the degree of personal involvement in the functioning of the institution. Much research indicates that if, by his own choice, an individual engages in an action, he will tend to believe that the consequences of the action are desirable.[30] The evaluation of the consequences of one's own free actions justifies one's decision.

[30] Jack Brehm and Arthur R. Cohen, *Explorations in Cognitive Dissonance* (New York: John Wiley and Sons, 1962).

The greater freedom which members of an organization perceive themselves to have in coming to decisions, the more they will believe in the value of their activities.[31] Also, the greater effort and hard work required, the more highly valued will be the consequences of that work.[32] All of these processes functioned at Crest, especially in the early years. The ward staff were free to make many decisions in the hour-by-hour treatment of patients; and they made significant contribution to major staff decisions. And, finally, work on the ward was often taxing and sometimes painful.

A commitment to an institution, a group, or a job can help sustain hope in an institution in the face of discouraging or ambiguous facts. Whether loyalty is to the ideology or to the group makes little difference, so long as the individual members are committed to work for it.

The strength of commitment to Crest as an institution was manifest in other ways than in the dedication with which involved individuals carried out their duties. Threats to the institution were countered with a strong defense; for example, when Dr. Dunn's behavior as director of the hospital began to change, the professional people to whom he had delegated authority assumed many of his leadership functions.

A most striking illustration occurred in Crest's final year, when the outcome of Mr. Ullman's treatment became a test case for the value of Dr. Doren's new, eclectic treatment philosophy. The willingness of some of the professional and ward staff to consider Dr. Doren's ideology as a way of sustaining Crest shows that these people had not only developed a loyalty to the ideology, but to the institution as well.

A final source of strength for the ideology of an institution is

---

[31] Rensis Likert has assembled much data which suggests that workers produce more if they feel free to make work decisions either alone or in a group, when such decisions are felt to be within their competence. Likert, *New Patterns of Management* (New York: McGraw-Hill Book Co., 1961).

[32] Elliott Aronson and Judson Mills, "The Effect of Severity of Initiation on Liking for a Group," *Journal of Abnormal and Social Psychology*, LIX (1959), 177–81; Bertram H. Raven and Martin Fishbein, "Acceptance of Punishment and Change in Belief," *Journal of Abnormal and Social Psychology*, LXIII (1961), 188–90.

leadership. Strength comes not only from a leader propounding the ideology per se, but from his hopefulness, personal drive, and dedication. Crest's founders and early directors shared these qualities. All felt that the hospital should and would grow and develop into an important, self-sufficient, dynamic institution. Members of the Board of Trustees and hospital staff were infected with the excitement of these men.

The significance of leadership for the hospital was, perhaps, most obvious when the hospital leadership lacked dedicated enthusiasm. Then, the hopefulness and morale of all persons connected with the hospital declined. The trustees were crushed by the attack on Dr. Dunn and by his resignation. The board could not regain its early fire while Dr. Dale was the passive acting director, nor could it become enthusiastic when the leadership of the hospital was taken over by a group of consultants. Finally, Dr. Doren's mild leadership could not revive hopefulness.

For the hospital staff, Dr. Dunn's erratic behavior and withdrawal set in motion a steady process of decline of morale. Dr. Dale was unenthusiastic about his job; and he withdrew his close support of the ward staff. Miss Nichol's lessening interest in the ward staff was a further blow. During the "adolescent rebellion," the ward staff directly attributed their ineffectuality to the lack of support from the professionals. The ward staff felt that the doctors, as a group, did not have the "answer" to the problem of the adolescents; Miss Nichols admitted her inadequacy. The staff's perception of inadequacy in the professional leadership resulted in a loss of confidence in its own abilities, which, in turn, snowballed into the disaster of the adolescent rebellion.

The failure of Dr. Doren's administration to arrest the downward trend of morale was the result of a combination of factors. Dr. Doren lacked the vigor and drive of the more successful directors. He de-emphasized the significance of the ward staff. Doren's eclecticism undermined the ideology of many of the hospital staff; psychological treatment no longer was accorded a unique status. Another factor undermining the ward staff's confidence was the confusion due to the overlapping authority of Drs. Doren and Preston. Staff members could not feel certain about their work when the director indicated his lack of complete confidence in Dr. Preston. Finally, Dr. Doren was not aware that staff morale was very low.

Crucial support for an ideology comes from a leader who is not vulnerable to the upsets of patients. In some cases this leadership may come from someone who is on the ward, one who has strong convictions about the effectiveness of his approach. Wilmer, who reported his experience as director of an admitting ward in a Naval hospital, typifies such a person.[33] He believed in the power of positive expectations of patients; he communicated this philosophy to his staff; his beliefs determined his policies on the ward, and they dramatically affected patient behavior. The hopefulness of the leader can influence the staff by many routes: if he is perceived as an expert, they will believe in the future of the institution if he does; they might identify with him; and his confidence might spread to each member of the institution.

The fact that the leader has confidence in himself in no way leads to his having less confidence in others; the reverse is true. Much empirical work has indicated that people tend to perceive others in much the same way that they perceive themselves;[34] a person who has a high evaluation of himself tends to have a high evaluation of others. This is especially true if the others are of the same type of person or belong to the same group; for example, the people in the institution.[35] Drs. Dean, Jones, Davidson, and Dunn believed strongly in the type of treatment offered at Crest and in their own abilities to foster and expand it. They also had great confidence in the ward staff. On the other hand, Dr. Doren did not have strong convictions about Crest, the ward staff, or his personal ability to be a "saviour."

One of the few characteristics that have been found in leaders of a wide variety of groups is self-confidence.[36] Self-confidence is

[33] Harry A. Wilmer, *Social Psychiatry in Action* (Springfield, Ill.: Charles C. Thomas Co., 1958).

[34] Jerome S. Bruner and Renato Taguiri, "The Perception of People" in *Handbook of Social Psychology*, Vol. II, ed. Gardner Lindsey (Cambridge, Mass.: Addison Wesley Publishing Co., 1954).

[35] Ezra Stotland, Alvin Zander, and Thomas Natsoulas, "Generalization of Interpersonal Similarity," *Journal of Abnormal and Social Psychology*, LXII (1961), 250–56.

[36] Cecil A. Gibb, "Leadership," in *Handbook of Social Psychology*.

necessary to a person who assumes responsibilities of leadership and for his acceptance of the challenge of the position. Leaders may seek the role because of their self-confidence; but, also, members of a group may push them into leadership positions because they sense that a leader should be self-confident. An additional factor may be that the group members realize that they often depend on the self-confidence of the leader for their own confidence in the group and in themselves as part of the group. The leader's confidence effectively communicates the tone that a setback is not a disaster, that hope is valid, that difficulties are only temporary. It has already been emphasized that it is not the behavior of a person per se which is important, but the interpretation, the meaning of the behavior for the future. Likewise, in a group, the meaning attached to a setback is more important than the setback itself. And the leader may play a critical role in defining this meaning.

The importance of enthusiastic, confident leaders who believe strongly in the ideology may be best illustrated if these types of leaders are contrasted with more reasonable, flexible, "realistic" ones. The latter are concerned with the "facts," with a variety of viewpoints, with balance and moderation. Dr. Doren epitomizes this approach; he felt that the choice of therapy for each patient should be flexible and eclectic. It is hard to quarrel with such reasonableness, but it is difficult to be inspired by it. It is a common finding in social psychology that the more extreme a person's attitude, the more involved he is in it.[37] To gain involvement and dedication, it is often necessary to be extreme, to reject moderation, and to take a firm stand for a point of view. Such positions often entail a rejection of empiricism. Many studies have shown that people with strong opinions avoid situations in which they might encounter facts opposed to their position.[38]

The importance of a dedicated leader in therapeutic com-

[37] Edward A. Suchman, "The Intensity Component in Attitude and Opinion Research" in Samuel A. Stouffer, *et al*, *Measurement and Prediction* (Princeton, N.J.: Princeton University Press, 1950).

[38] Herbert H. Hyman and Paul B. Sheatsley, "Some Reasons Why Information Campaigns Fail," *Public Opinion Quarterly*, II (1947), 412–23.

munities like Crest has been emphasized by Mabel Blake Cohen, who writes:

> In contrasting the successful (therapeutic) communities with the much more frequent failures, the factor which seems to stand out most vividly is that of belief. In the successes there is consistently a dedicated leader who sparks the whole community hierarchy with hope, expectation of improvement, a sense of knowing what to do and how to do it. Is this really the basis of success in the therapeutic community? Does the organizational form of the community matter as fundamentally as this more intangible morale factor? What happens to therapeutic communities when the leader dies or moves away? Does the structure provide a sufficient carry over to maintain the social system as a going concern, or does it relapse into a routine institution of whatever kind it may be? Do the staff members who have developed under the leader acquire a basic attitude or set of skills which permits the community to continue to thrive? Is there anything in the way in which the staff experiences the community which is an attitude-changing, or, in other words, a therapeutic experience and which therefore permits continuity? There are no systematic data to answer these questions. Nevertheless, the impression exists that when the dedicated leader is gone the community settles down to something hum-drum.[39]

Therapeutic communities are normative organizations, and are characterized by a high degree of commitment to the ideology on the part of members. This has consequences for the nature of leadership; leaders will be evaluated and accepted or rejected in terms of their effectiveness in achieving the goals of the institution; that is, in terms of their ability to articulate the goals of the institution and to indicate ways of achieving them. This type of leadership has been termed task leadership. The acceptance of the leader, then, is less contingent on his formal

[39] Mabel Blake Cohen, "The Therapeutic Community and Therapy," *Psychiatry*, XX (1957), 173–75.

status or other aspects of his behavior such as his ability to function as a social-emotional leader (a leader primarily concerned with interpersonal relationships among members of the institution), or his administrative ability (the coordination of the housekeeping functions of the institution). At Crest the evaluation and acceptance of leaders in terms of their ability as task leaders was seen, especially in the early years, when the formal definition of leadership was often ignored. Drs. Dean and Jones shared leadership of the infant organization, and Miss Nichols, with little formal authority, was always a significant leader.[40]

The high level of commitment characteristic of normative institutions like Crest always has consequences for leadership. A leader might be replaced by another, or another person may function as leader without the formal trappings of office. The change of a leader is contingent upon there being someone in the organization who is motivated to function as task leader, and upon the willingness of others to accept him as a leader. Such potential leaders are more likely to be found in normative groups, for with their high level of commitment to the group and ideology, potential leaders would be more sensitive to the inadequacy of the leader and more motivated to replace him.

In remunerative groups, the members may not be motivated to replace the leader if they are receiving sufficient remuneration, regardless of the effectiveness of the leader in helping the group achieve its goals. His effectiveness might be a matter of indifference to members of the institution. A new leader in a remunerative group could more easily lower or change the goals of the organization, and is more likely to be motivated to do so than in a normative group. Obviously, a parallel argument can be applied in analyzing coercive groups. In short, then, in a normative group it is likely that inadequate task leaders will be replaced to the extent that the formal structure of the organization permits such flexibility. Essentially, this is what occurred

---

[40] Donald C. Pelz found that in a scientific research organization the researchers accepted close supervision from a leader whom they respected highly as a scientist, but rejected supervision from a less competent scientist. Pelz, "Some Social Factors Related to Performance in a Research Organization," *Administrative Science Quarterly*, I (1956), 310–25.

when Dr. Dunn's "adequacy" declined and the other professionals took over for him. In remunerative and coercive groups, it is unlikely that a similar process would occur; leaders are replaced for different reasons: for example, for power purposes.

Another implication of this analysis is that the greater the level of commitment of the members of an organization, the less impact will a change of leadership, formal or informal, have on them. Members of the group have a lesser need for inspiration coming from a leader; they have their own resources of commitment. Dr. Davidson's departure had little impact on the functioning of Crest. He was quickly replaced, and the high and general commitment to the hospital continued.[41]

The preceding analysis is predicated on the assumption that a new leader of a normative group will share its norms. Should the leader not share the ideology, the commitment of the members of the organization to the ideology becomes a source of conflict. This would most frequently occur in formally organized institutions, in which the leader is chosen by another agency or by some formal procedure. Such was the case in the choice of Dr. Doren. He was an outsider; he was chosen by an outside group—the consultants; he was not involved with the Crest ideology; and he was not chosen for his ability as a leader, but because of his experience as a psychoanalyst. Many of his difficulties with the ward and professional staff were attributable to his lack of adherence to the Crest way, either in administrative practices or in philosophy of treatment.[42]

[41] Ronald Lippitt and Robert K. White found that members of groups with democratic leaders encouraged all members to participate in discussions and thereby become committed to the group goals. When the leader was not present, the members continued to work. Lippitt and White, "An Experiment Study of Leadership and Group Life," in *Readings in Social Psychology*, eds. Eleanor Maccoby, Theodore M. Newcomb, and Eugene L. Hartley (New York: Holt, Rinehart, and Winston, 1958).

[42] Doren's situation was like that of persons in Ferenc Merei's study who had some experience with leadership, but who were introduced into an already functioning group. Their attempts to exercise leadership were rebuffed by the group. Merei, "Group Leadership and Institutionalization," *Human Relations*, II (1949), 23–39. Edward P. Hollander has pointed out that innovations will be accepted in a group from those who have been in the group for a long time. Thus, some of the persons involved in Merei's

Another implication of the present analysis relates to the influence of an individual leader on an institution. A director is neither helpless, totally swept by forces beyond his control, nor is he able to change radically the development of an organization simply because he is sufficiently motivated. The issue of the potential influence of the individual member is particularly salient with regard to leadership; how much do the personal characteristics and motivations of a leader influence the course of development of an organization? In a normative group, with a flexible leadership structure and a high level of commitment from all members of the organization, the ability of a leader to influence the development of the organization is limited in special ways. Crest was an institution with a moderately flexible leadership structure. While the head nurse could exercise leadership, and suggestions for treatment could flow upward within the organization, the formal requirement that the director be a psychiatrist limited the flexibility of the leadership structure. In such an organization the leader can be quite significant, although in the short run, the fact that the leadership structure is somewhat flexible permits inadequacies to be compensated for by others in the organization. But, as demonstrated by the consequences of Dr. Dunn's difficulties, the effectiveness of such compensation is temporary. Dr. Dale's reluctance as acting director had unhappy effects on the hospital, and Dr. Doren's leadership failed to revive Crest. On the other hand, in the early years, the founders and first directors had tremendous influence.

One need not choose between an omnipotent leader theory or a completely situation-oriented theory, but one must consider the many factors that determine the extent of a leader's influence. Cohen is right and wrong. A dedicated, enthusiastic leader is important for the maintenance of a hopeful ideology in an institution. But he can be replaced by others without the institution becoming "hum-drum," and he needs other sources of support if his drive is to be effectual.

---

study proceeded to accept the group's norms, probably so that they could be accepted in the leadership role. Hollander, "Conformity, Status, and Idiosyncrasy Credit," *Psychological Review*, LXV (1958), 117–27.

Relationships Among the Sources of a Hopeful Ideology

Only a limited number of sources are salient at a given time in an institution. This limitation is a result of several factors. First, the involved people are not able to respond to more than a limited number of aspects of their environment. Second, some people may not be prone or even able to respond to some sources. Some may be skeptical about experts; others may be cynical about a source of reflected charisma. Third, some of the sources may be more "active" or pertinent than others. For example, the experts may not be in a position to communicate their support nor feel any special motivation to do so; some people may have been "graduates" of the institutional source of reflected charisma, while others may have no knowledge of it; the leadership of an institution may be so dynamic that people do not notice the lack of expansion of physical plant.

The greater power of some factors than of others at certain times is clear in the history of Crest. During the institution's infancy, the reflected charisma from Menningers was most prominent, more so than the educative source of support which needed time to evolve. During Davidson's administration, the support from experts in the community was rejected; but the emergence of new supports, i.e., strong leadership and increased professional staff, compensated for the lack of expert support.

What happens when a significant source of hopefulness ceases to function? What if a leader is lost; experts are rejected; the institution stops growing; or the community becomes indifferent? The loss of one or a few sources of hopefulness may not have any detrimental effects on the institution. For one, the sources of hope can substitute for one another; when one is weak or absent, another source may function in its stead. Also, there is a ceiling for hopefulness. The degree of confidence that the institution is going to achieve its goals may reach one hundred per cent certainty with two or three sources of hopefulness. By the same token, the loss of one or two sources may not lead to a drop below one hundred per cent certainty. For example, reflected charisma declined in significance during the first few years of Crest, yet hope was maintained at a high level. The loss of expert support during Davidson's administration did not affect the spirit of the hospital. His leadership, the growth of the hospital, the educational process, and the ego-value of the ideology more than filled the gap.

What happens when a large number of meaningful supports for an institution fail at the same time? This occurred at Crest after Dunn's departure. The leadership had become weak; the expansion of the hospital had ceased; community support as reflected in an enthusiastic board was no more; education of the ward staff declined. In such a situation, potential sources of support, which had not been salient, become so. They may arise as a result of the normal functioning of an organization; for example, a nonprofit foundation, short of funds, will turn to the community; or a Board of Trustees, not having the professional guidance of a director, will turn to other professionals. Also, people may feel a commitment to the institution and may be strongly motivated to continue as part of it, even in the face of the loss of hopefulness. Their motivation may be remunerative in the broadest sense, including both material and ego-satisfaction needs. Recognizing, however indirectly, that hope is necessary for the functioning and viability of the organization, they may attempt to find additional sources of hopefulness. In fact, members of an institution, individually or collectively, may try to increase the power of some potential sources of support which have not been conspicuous up to that point.

It may be that the potential sources of hope are not available; or, since they had not been vital, it was not perceived that they actually were negative and hopeless, and this is discovered only when they are looked to for help. The history of Crest is the story of potential sources of hopefulness that "collapsed" when they were needed as a consequence of the loss of other supports. When the board turned to the experts for help, they encountered division and negative attitudes. When the hospital staff expected a "saviour" in Doren, they discovered a reasonable man. When the hospital needed support from the local experts, they found a decline in referrals. When the hospital staff turned to the board as symbols of community support, they met weakness and ineffectuality. When they looked for evidence of expansion of the hospital, they found professional people leaving and a half-built building.

For an institution to be viable, either as a mundane or an aspiring group, it needs a variety of sources of hopefulness. Some may be salient at the same time; others may not, but must be capable of functioning as a support if the significant ones weaken or disappear. The absence of such reserves of sources may not be evident to many of the people involved until they are needed. At Crest, latent weakness existed for many years, but did not become important until the reserve sources of hopefulness were tapped. The rift within the psychiatric community occurred early in the history of Crest, but did not affect it markedly until Dunn's administration. The same is true of the difficulties caused by the conflict with Bell. The roots of the difficulties were planted early, but bore their bitter fruit years later.

Change of Normative Organizations to Other Types

An individual may develop commitment to a number of aspects of an institution: to the institution itself, to its ideology, to his part in his group, and to his job. Let us assume that the degree of commitment to each of these varies with time and person. Let us further assume that support for the ideology begins to weaken: support from reflected charisma from another institution is gone; leadership is poor; the social process is disturbed; and factual supports for the ideology are tottering. As a consequence, a member's commitment to the ideology of such a normative institution would be weakened. If the individual continues to be part of the organization, the source of his motivation would be something other than his commitment to the ideology. Other motivations, not so important before, may become relatively more important, even if they do not change in absolute magnitude. The members' loyalty to the institution and to their peers may become relatively more significant. However, if the institution has suffered enough serious blows to undermine the ideology, the commitment to the institution may be similarly undermined. In that case, other motivations, those related to a person's involvement in and commitment to the job, may become more salient; these may include monetary, status, or security issues. They have influenced the person before his commitment to the ideology and institution weakened, but now are free to influence him without the conflicts or inhibitions resulting from the normative demands. The institution will then be in the process of developing into a remunerative one; the individual is working for material and ego-satisfactions.[43]

Normative organizations which lose the supports for their ideologies tend to become remunerative ones.[44] This proposition closely parallels Bales' idea that when an organization faces a series of threats or frustrations, the members will tend to engage in behavior designed to maintain their security. The present argument differs from Bales in holding that the sources of changed behavior are the emergence of motives which remained submerged under the normative commitment. The processes referred to by Bales do occur; the processes described above also occur, but have not been sufficiently recognized.

Regardless of its other effects, the rise of a remunerative orientation functions to sustain an organization during a difficult period, after which hope might be regained. In fact, in Crest, the rise of a more remunerative orientation was concomitant with a residual sense of hopefulness—hope that the future would somehow be better than the present. It is possible for normative organizations to become coercive rather than remunerative, but this is improbable in the setting in which most normative organizations function.

Crest was clearly a normative institution with a high degree of commitment from people at all levels until the middle of Dunn's administration. From the time of the change in Dr. Dunn, supports for the ideology and the institution grew steadily weaker. Dr. Clark's attack on Dunn and the hospital led to the loss of expert support. The withdrawal of support by the Columbia Clinic resulted in a significant decline in referrals and a consequent loss of income. Staff had to be reduced; the new building could not be completed; a new director was not found, and the promotion of Dale removed a strong leader from the ward staff.

[43] Etzioni, *A Comparative Analysis of Complex Organizations.*
[44] Bales, *Interaction Process Analysis.*

In a relatively short time, many of the ward staff's supports for the ideology were removed. An increase of remunerative aspects followed. Concern for status rose on the wards; nurses vied with aides and old aides with new aides. Ward personnel followed hospital rules and prescriptions in a more rigid, mechanical way; they seemed to find satisfaction in the rigid performance of role, rather than in their therapeutic effectiveness. A few months after Dunn departed, the aides threatened to strike for higher wages. Off-grounds parties became "orgies" rather than ways of integrating and educating newcomers to the group. During the suicide epidemic, aides refused responsibilities for patients defined as "suicidal." The motivations for these behaviors were clearly "remunerative."[45] The kind of effort to achieve security, which Bales holds occurs in the face of threat to the group, probably also took place, but the data just cited are highly consistent with the present analysis. In all likelihood, both processes were occurring in different degrees at different times to different people.

The absence of a normative orientation to the hospital clearly could lead to a decline in the effectiveness of the treatment program. The ideology had been one of hope, and it was believed that Crest was a superior institution, which, by means of psychological treatment, could cure anyone. With the threats to the ideology, hopefulness declined. The effects on the patients were devastating: the adolescent rebellion and the epidemic of suicide. The example of Crest underscores the proposition that in normative organizations a failure of support for the norms and for the institution leads to a rise of remunerative orientations which are not functional for the organization.

Dependency and Autonomy

One of the pervasive themes running through the story of Crest is that of a person or group seeking help from another. The purpose of Crest was to give help; the givers of help to patients in turn sought help from other lay and professional groups, who in turn, sought help from others. A price is most often paid for help. One type of price sometimes paid is involvement in many other aspects of the help-giver's life, some of which may be pain-

[45] *Ibid.*

ful or frustrating to the person who is aided. For example, when the trustees turned to the consultants for help late in Crest's life, the organization of the Board of Trustees itself had to be changed. The consultants' demand that Dr. Crawford be removed from the Board of Trustees was a consequence of the long-standing rift between Drs. Clark and Crawford.

Another important instance of this process concerns the need of a nonprofit hospital for financial support from the community. In order to secure the funds with which to open the hospital, the Crest founders turned to Mr. Bell. This had several consequences, unintended by the founders. First, Mr. Bell's goals for the hospital became a source of conflict with the founders during the first few years. Second, by going to Mr. Bell for funds, they cut themselves off from other potential sources of help in the community. Mr. Bell strongly discouraged any attempts to secure funds from philanthropists more wealthy than he; and his refusal to change his contribution from a loan to a gift made it difficult to approach others for funds. This difficulty does not appear unique to Crest. Belknap and Steinle[46] report that hospitals in one community were unable to secure assistance from a variety of sources in the community because it was sponsored by a minority religious group. This group could be depended on for continuing support, but its available resources were limited. In another community studied by Belknap and Steinle, the founder of the main hospital had access to powerful and wealthy groups, whose continued support he secured for the hospital. Thus, the price here was minimal. Belknap and Steinle conclude that the crucial difference between the two communities was the unity and dedication of the leadership structure. In one, the main hospital was supported by a powerful and unified group of leaders. In the other, the leadership was not only divided along religious lines, but the community was subordinate politically to county government. The first community, on the contrary, dominated the county government.

Another type of price that can be paid for help relates to autonomy. Help can be given which supports the autonomy or independence of the receiver of the help; the need is viewed as

[46] Belknap and Steinle, *The Community and Its Hospitals.*

temporary, as resulting from a difficulty which can be overcome. The receiver is regarded as essentially sound, strong, reliable, and healthy; he will be able to continue to function independently and autonomously in the future. On the other hand, help can be extended with the implication that the receiver is weak and essentially dependent. The need for help is expected to persist, and the helping relationship is seen as a long-term one. The acceptance of such help, then, implies a loss of autonomy and self-respect by the receiver.

The attitude of the helper is extremely important in determining whether the receiver will view dependency as destructive of autonomy. The giver may convey the expectation that the receipt of help implies a loss of autonomy. When the consultants began to help Crest in the last years, they took the view that the hospital was "sick" and needed "therapy." The consultants' view of Crest as a sick institution was, in part, a consequence of the fact that the trustees turned to them only in crises; while not necessarily an inaccurate evaluation of the difficulties in the hospital, the attitude was also an outgrowth of the way psychiatrists often function professionally. Their role with a patient centers around the latter's "illness"; and often, *all* of the patient's behavior is seen as potentially affected by the illness. Accordingly, the attitude with which the consultants assisted the hospital implied that the difficulties were not temporary, and that the hospital was basically "sick." This view was manifest in a number of ways: the consultants quickly established a system by which all psychotherapists at the hospital would be under supervision; they discharged the leading psychotherapist at the hospital, much to the dismay of the hospital staff and other professional persons; finally, shortly after Doren's arrival, they set up a committee to examine the very necessity for a hospital like Crest.

In treating patients, the absence of a hopeful expectation on the part of the treating person makes improvement difficult.[47] The same is true with regard to help given to an institution. The failure of morale to rise at Crest during the last two years of its existence was partially due to the ways in which the hospital was aided. This help contrasts sharply with that given in the early

[47] See the discussion on pp. 221 ff.

years of the hospital, when the consultants conveyed great confidence in the hospital staff. At that time the help they gave the hospital was not construed by them to be help for a "patient-like" institution, but advice to a strong, growing institution, which needed guidance to become autonomous.

The effects of expectations were evident within the hospital as well. Dr. Doren did not share the attitude of his predecessors that his ward staff was a highly qualified, semiprofessional group, but held that any warm decent person could be as effective as a member of the ward staff. The morale and effectiveness of the ward staff declined.

In the early years, the part-time medical directors and consultants spent only a few hours each day at the hospital. They gave Miss Nichols, and implicitly the ward staff, great freedom to make decisions about patients. They wished to keep psychiatrists who did not agree with the Crest view out of the hospital; but they allowed the ward staff to do the "ejecting." This enhanced the power and autonomy of the ward staff. Drs. Davidson and Dunn devoted much of their efforts to expanding the hospital, leaving the day-to-day running of the hospital in the hands of the staff. During these years the hospital staff was most committed to the Crest ideology and morale at the hospital was highest.

When a great amount of help is given a person or an institution, it often defines the receiver as weak, and requires dependence. The hospital patient lives in a "total institution," wherein he is directed at all times, and is dependent in all aspects of his life. The effect of such "total help" in destroying the patient's self-esteem and feelings of autonomy has been demonstrated.[48]

In summary, too much help, and certain attitudes of the helper, can transform a helping relationship into one facilitating dependency, and loss of autonomy, self-respect, and confidence. In the history of Crest, many well intended actions had this effect. But the ideology of Crest was one of high confidence and self-respect; the depreciating effects of the helping relationships undermined the Crest ideology. These same factors are important with regard to aiding patients. Patients depend on the staff

[48] Erwin Goffmann, *Asylums* (New York: Doubleday and Co., 1961).

for help; this help can be hopeful and respectful, implying autonomy; or it can be hopeless, implying essential dependency. The ways in which the hospital staff help patients are influenced by the ways in which the staff are helped by their superiors.[49] Obviously, the issue of autonomy is closely bound up with hopefulness. A hospital which is secure in its autonomy faces its future hopefully, and helps its patients. And that, of course, is its essential purpose.

The history of Crest has illustrated the vast variety of factors which separately and in complex interaction can influence the degree of hopefulness and the viability of institutions in general. We hope that the practical and theoretical lessons can be found useful and valid in other settings.

[49] Katz and Kahn, "Leadership Practices . . .," *Group Dynamics*, found that the lower-level supervisors in a factory exercise leadership similarly to the way they themselves are supervised.